UCSMP
SCOTT, FORESMAN

The University of Chicago School Mathematics Project

Precalculus and Discrete Mathematics

Quizzes and Test Masters

- Quizzes
- Chapter Tests Forms, A and B
- Cumulative Chapter Tests
- Four Comprehensive Tests (Chapters 1–3, 1–6, 1–9, and 1–13)
- Answers included

Scott, Foresman
Editorial Offices: Glenview, Illinois Regional Offices: Sunnyvale, California •
Tucker, Georgia • Glenview, Illinois • Oakland, New Jersey • Dallas, Texas

Contents

Quiz for Lessons 1-1 Through 1-3

1. *Multiple choice.* Which is true?
   (a) ∃ *real number x such that* $\sqrt{x} \geq 0$.
   (b) ∀ *real numbers x,* $\sqrt{x} \geq 0$.

1. _____

2. Write the negation of the statement
   All trapezoids have a right angle.

2. _____

3. Write the truth table for the logical expression *p or (~q).*

3.

p	q		

4. According to De Morgan's Laws, *(p and ~q)* is equivalent to ____?____.

4. _____

5. Use a counterexample to show that the following statement is false.
   ∀ *real numbers x,* $\frac{1}{x} < 1$.

5. _____

6. If *p(x)* is the sentence $(x + 5)^2 = x^2 + 10x + 25$, give the sentence $p(\sqrt{3})$.

6. _____

7. For what truth values of *p* and *q* is *(p and q)* false?

7. _____

_____

8. *Multiple choice.* A traffic sign at an intersection states:
   No left turn from 4 to 6 PM on weekdays.
   Let *p* be the statement *It is between 4 and 6 PM.*
   Let *q* be the statement *It is a weekday.*
   Which statement below best describes the times when left turns are allowed?
   (a) *p and q*   (b) *p or q*
   (c) *~p and ~q*   (d) *~p or ~q*

8. _____

9. The chart below gives information about three towns.

Name	Population	Elementary Schools	Secondary Schools
Middletown	72,000	29	5
Centerville	39,500	17	3
Valley Ridge	43,000	21	4

Is the following statement *true* or *false*? Justify your answer.
   ∃ *town t such that the population of t is* > 40,000 *and t has* < 25 *schools.*

9. _____

_____

_____

10. Give an example of a universal statement.

10. _____

Quiz for Lessons 1-4 Through 1-6

1. Complete the input-output table for the following network.

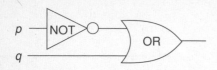

1.

p	q	output
1	1	
1	0	
0	1	
0	0	

2. Write a logical expression that corresponds to the following network.

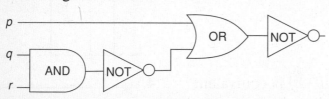

2. _____

3. Write the negation of the statement
If the sun sets, then the wind dies down.

3. _____

4. a. Write the statement *Every good boy does fine* in *if-then* form.

4. a. _____

_____

b. Under what circumstances would the statement in part **a** be false?

b. _____

_____

5. *Multiple choice.* Which statement below is the contrapositive of $5^x > 125 \Rightarrow x > 3$?

(a) $5^x \not> 125 \Rightarrow x \not> 3$
(b) $x \not> 3 \Rightarrow 5^x \not> 125$
(c) $x > 3 \Rightarrow 5^x > 125$

5. _____

6. Consider the argument:

If you forget to add baking soda to your cake batter,
  then the cake will not rise.
Pat baked a cake that did not rise.
∴ *Pat forgot to add baking soda to the batter.*

Is the argument valid? Why or why not?

6. _____

_____

7. Consider the premises:

If you have an English paper due, then you stay up
  late working on it.
Whenever you are up late, you make popcorn.

a. Draw a valid conclusion.

7. a. _____

_____

b. Name the form of the argument.

b. _____

Quiz for Lessons 1-4 Through 1-6 (page 2)

3

8. Write the two *if-then* statements that are contained in the statement

    The graph of $y = ax^2 + bx + c$ opens upward if and only if $a > 0$.

8. _____

_____

_____

_____

_____

9. Determine the output of the program below if the numbers -5 and 2 are input for A and B.

```
10   INPUT A, B
20   IF A * B > 0 THEN PRINT "SAME"
        ELSE PRINT "DIFFERENT"
30   END
```

9. _____

Chapter 1 Test, Form A

In 1 and 2, select the best description of each sentence:
  (a) statement   (b) universal statement
  (c) existential statement   (d) none of these.

1. $x^3 + 6 = 12$

1. _____

2. *All mammals give live birth to their young.*

2. _____

3. **a.** Simplify $\sqrt{8} \cdot \sqrt{18}$.

3. a. _____

  b. What universal statement was used to answer part **a**?

b. _____

_____

4. *True* or *false*? $\exists$ *a real number z such that* $z^4 = -16$.

4. _____

5. Rewrite $5 < x \le 7$ by writing out the implied *and* and *or*.

5. _____

In 6 and 7, write the negation of the statement.

6. *All symphony orchestras employ a full-time tuba player.*

6. _____

_____

_____

7. *I will go to the concert and I will not go to the restaurant.*

7. _____

_____

_____

8. Write the following statement in *if-then* form.
  No student with a temperature higher than 99.6° shall remain in school.

8. _____

_____

_____

9. Consider the statement
  If the president's speech is a success, then the proposal will be approved.
  Under what circumstances would this be a false statement?

9. _____

_____

_____

10. *Multiple choice.* Determine the statement that is logically equivalent to
  If it is the Sunday paper, then the comics are in color.

  (a) *If it is not the Sunday paper, then the comics are not in color.*
  (b) *If the comics are in color, then it is the Sunday paper.*
  (c) *If the comics are not in color, then it is not the Sunday paper.*

10. _____

Chapter 1 Test, Form A (page 2)

In 11 and 12, tell whether the argument is valid or invalid.
Support your answer with a reference to one of the following.
  (a) Law of detachment (*modus ponens*)
  (b) Law of Indirect Reasoning (*modus tollens*)
  (c) Law of Transitivity
  (d) Converse Error
  (e) Inverse Error
  (f) Improper Induction

11. *If k is even, then k + 1 is odd.*
     5 is odd.
   ∴ *4 is even.*

11. _____

12. *If the comic strip is Peanuts, then the dog's name is*
     Snoopy.
     The comic strip is Peanuts.
   ∴ *The dog's name is Snoopy.*

12. _____

In 13 and 14, tell if the statement is *true* or *false*. If it is true,
prove it. If it is false, disprove it by giving a counterexample.

13. *If n is an even integer, then $n^2 + 1$ is an odd integer.*

13. _____

14. *If $n^2 - n$ is an even integer, then n is an even integer.*

14. _____

15. *True* or *false*? The negation of a statement of the form $\exists\, x$
    in S such that $p(x)$ is a statement of the form $\exists\, x$ in S
    such that $\sim p(x)$.

15. _____

Chapter 1 Test, Form A   (page 3)

16. Given the statements $p(x)$: $x^2 < 5$ and $q(x)$: $x > 2$,
    determine the truth value of $\sim(\sim p(-6) \text{ or } q(-6))$.

    16. _____

17. Draw a valid conclusion from these premises.

    If a triangle is right, then two of its angles are
    complementary.
    In $\triangle PQR$, no two angles are complementary.

    17. _____

    _____

18. Determine the output of the following computer program
    if $N = 18$.

    18. _____

    ```
    10   INPUT N
    20   IF (N > 10 AND N < 15) OR N < 0
            THEN PRINT "IT CHECKS"
    30   PRINT "END"
    ```

19. Write the logical expression that corresponds to the
    network pictured below.

    19. _____

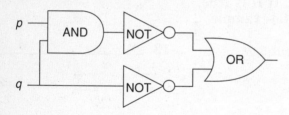

20. Write a truth table for $\sim(p \Rightarrow q)$.

    20.
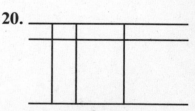

21. Write a truth table to show that
    $\sim(p \text{ or } q) \equiv \sim p \text{ and } \sim q$.

    21.
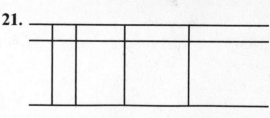

Precalculus and Discrete Mathematics © Scott, Foresman and Company

Chapter 1 Test, Form B

In 1 and 2, select the best description of each sentence:
  (a) statement   (b) universal statement
  (c) existential statement   (d) none of these.

1. *Some cars use diesel fuel.*   1. _____

2. $3x < 4 - 5x$ 2. _____

3. a. Factor $4c^2 - 9$.   3. a. _____

    b. What universal statement was used to answer part **a**?   b. _____

                                                                    _____

4. *True* or *false*? ∀ *real numbers y, y < y + 1.*   4. _____

5. Rewrite $-2 \le x < 0$, by writing out the implied *and* and *or*.   5. _____

In 6 and 7, write the negation of the statement.

6. *All entrants are adults or are accompanied by a parent.*   6. _____

                                                                      _____

                                                                      _____

7. *Some people leave nothing on their plate when they eat.*   7. _____

                                                                       _____

                                                                      _____

8. Write the following statement in *if-then* form.   8. _____
    Groups of 10 or more people will be charged a 15%
    gratuity.

                                                                       _____

                                                                      _____

9. Consider the statement   9. _____
    A person is eligible for enrollment at the university only
    if the person is a high school graduate.

Under what circumstances would this be a false statement?   _____

10. *Multiple choice.* Determine the statement that is logically   10. _____
    equivalent to
        If it is the Sunday paper, then the paper has at least
        100 pages.
    (a) *If it is not the Sunday paper, then the paper has less*
        than 100 pages.
    (b) *If the paper has less than 100 pages, then it is not the*
        Sunday paper.
    (c) *If the paper has at least 100 pages, then it is the*
        Sunday paper.

Chapter 1 Test, Form B   (page 2)

In 11 and 12, tell whether the argument is valid or invalid.
Support your answer with a reference to one of the following.
  (a) Law of Detachment (*modus ponens*)
  (b) Law of Indirect Reasoning (*modus tollens*)
  (c) Law of Transitivity
  (d) Converse Error
  (e) Inverse Error
  (f) Improper Induction

11.   If $x^2 > 9$, then $x > 3$.
        $-4 \not> 3$
      $\therefore (-4)^2 \not> 9$

11. _____

12.   If today is Tuesday, then tomorrow is Wednesday.
        Today is not Tuesday.
      $\therefore$ Tomorrow is not Wednesday.

12. _____

In 13 and 14, tell if the statement is *true* or *false*. If it is true,
prove it. If it is false, disprove it by giving a counterexample.

13. If m is an even integer, then $\dfrac{m + 2}{2}$ is even.

13. _____

14. If a and b are odd integers, then $a(b + 1)$ is even.

14. _____

15. *True* or *false*? The negation of a statement of the form
    $\forall\ x$ in S, $p(x)$ is a statement of the form $\exists\ x$ in S such that
    $\sim p(x)$.

15. _____

                                   Precalculus and Discrete Mathematics © Scott, Foresman and Company

Chapter 1 Test, Form B   (page 3)

16. Given the statements $p(x)$: *2x is an odd integer* and $q(x)$:
x is a prime number, determine the truth value of $p(3)$
and $q(3)$.

16. _____

17. Draw a valid conclusion from these premises.
   If $x = 0$, then $xy = 0$.
   If $x^2 + y^2 = 0$, then $x = 0$.

17. _____

18. Determine the output of the following computer program
if -3 is input for G and 8 is input for L.

```
10   INPUT G, L
20   IF G < 0 AND (L < 5 OR L > 10) THEN
        PRINT "WHAT IS YOUR PROBLEM?"
30   IF NOT (G + L > 10) THEN PRINT "NO
        PROBLEM"
40   END
```

18. _____

19. Write the logical expression that corresponds to the
network pictured below.

19. _____

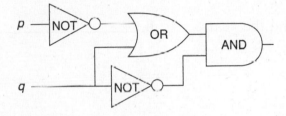

20. Write a truth table for *p or (~ q)*.

20.

21. Write a truth table to show that
   ~p or q ≡ ~(p and ~q).

21.

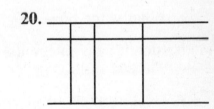

Quiz for Lessons 2-1 Through 2-3

You will need an automatic grapher for this quiz.

1. What is the domain of f if $f(x) = 5 + \sqrt{x + 12}$?

1. _____

In 2 and 3, refer to the chart at the right.

2. Let $a(x)$ = number of fatal accidents in year x and $b(x)$ = year in which x fatal accidents occurred. Which is not a function, a or b? Explain.

3. Let $d(x)$ be the number of departures in year x.

a. Find the largest interval on which d is decreasing.

U.S. Airline Safety

Year	Departures (millions)	Fatal Accidents
1976	4.8	2
1977	4.9	3
1978	5.0	5
1979	5.4	4
1980	5.3	0
1981	5.2	4
1982	5.0	3
1983	5.0	4
1984	5.4	1
1985	5.7	4
1986	6.4	2
1987	7.0	4

Source: *Statistical Abstract of the United States, 1987, 1990*

2. _____

_____

_____

_____

3. a. _____

b. Give the value of a relative minimum of d and the year in which it occurs.

b. _____

4. Consider the function g graphed at the right.

a. What is the range of g?

b. Identify any interval(s) where g is decreasing.

c. Is g a discrete function?

d. What is the minimum value of g?

4. a. _____

b. _____

c. _____

d. _____

5. A container manufacturer must make a rectangular box with a volume of 500 cubic centimeters. The end of the box must be twice as wide as it is high. Let x be the height of the box.

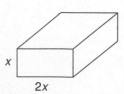

a. Express the length, l, of the box as a function of x.

5. a. _____

b. Write a function that gives the surface area, S, of the closed box as a function of x.

b. _____

c. Use a graph to find the height x that produces the minimum surface area (and therefore reduces costs).

c. _____

Quiz for Lessons 2-4 Through 2-6

You will need an automatic grapher for this quiz.

1. Consider the sequence defined by $a_n = \frac{5n}{n+1}$ ∀ *for* $n \geq 1$.

   a. List the first five terms of a.

   1. a. _____

   b. Does a appear to be increasing, decreasing, or neither?

   b. _____

   c. *True* or *false*? $\lim\limits_{n\to\infty} a_n = \frac{1}{5}$

   c. _____

2. Write $\lim\limits_{x\to-\infty} f(x) = 8$ in words.

   2. _____

   _____

3. Given the following four facts about the function g, sketch a possible graph of g on the grid at the right.

   g is an even function.
   $g(0) = 2$
   $g(1) = 1.5$
   $\lim\limits_{x\to\infty} g(x) = 1$

   3.

   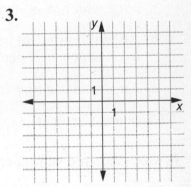

4. Let f be the function defined by $f(x) = 2 - \frac{1}{x^2}$.

   a. Sketch a graph of f.

   4. a.

   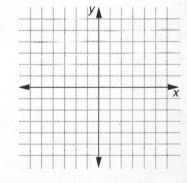

   b. Use limit notation to describe the end behavior of f.

   b. _____

   _____

   c. What is the domain of f?

   c. _____

5. Fred wins the lottery and receives $50,000. He invests this in an account that earns 14% interest compounded continuously. How many years will it take Fred's prize money to grow to $1 million?

   5. _____

Chapter 2 Test, Form A

You will need an automatic grapher for this test.

1. Let $f(x) = 2x^2 - 8x$.

   a. What is the minimum value of f?

   1. a. _____

   b. On what interval(s) is f decreasing?

   b. _____

2. What is the domain and range of the function $g(x) = 5 + \log x$?

   2. _____

3. Consider the function h graphed at the right.

   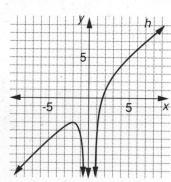

   a. Approximate the interval(s) over which h is increasing.

   3. a. _____

   b. Approximate the interval(s) over which h is decreasing.

   b. _____

   c. Approximate any relative maximum value to the nearest integer.

   c. _____

4. Consider the sequence $b_n = 8\left(\frac{1}{5}\right)^n$ for $n \geq 1$.

   a. Give the first three terms of b.

   4. a. _____

   b. What is $\lim\limits_{n \to \infty} b_n$?

   b. _____

5. Solve $\log_4 x = \frac{3}{2}$ for x.

   5. _____

6. Solve $\log_2 \frac{1}{32} = x$ for x.

   6. _____

7. Rewrite $\log\left(\frac{2x}{y}\right)$ in terms of $\log x$ and $\log y$.

   7. _____

8. Refer to the graph of the function f at the right.

   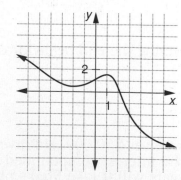

   a. Give all intervals on which f is decreasing.

   8. a. _____

   b. Give all intervals on which f is increasing.

   b. _____

   c. What appears to be the value of $\lim\limits_{x \to \infty} f(x)$?

   c. _____

   d. For what value of x is $f(x)$ a relative maximum?

   d. _____

Chapter 2 Test, Form A (page 2)

9. If you invest \$1,000 in a savings account that pays $5\frac{1}{4}\%$ interest compounded continuously, about how much will that amount become in 10 years?

9. _____

In 10 and 11, describe the end behavior of the function.

10. g, if $g(x) = 5^{-x}$

10. _____

_____

11. f, if $f(x) = -\left(\dfrac{\cos x}{x}\right)$

11. _____

_____

12. An open box is made from a rectangular piece of steel measuring 9 inches by 12 inches. A square with sides x inches long is cut from each corner and the flaps are folded up to form the sides of the box.

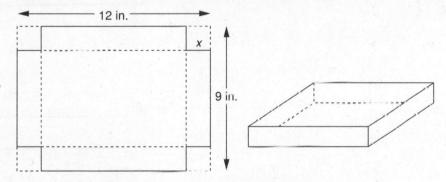

a. Express the length, l, of the base of the box as a function of x.

12. a. _____

b. Express the width, w, of the box as a function of x.

b. _____

c. Express the volume, V, of the box as a function of x.

c. _____

d. Sketch a graph of $V(x)$.

d.

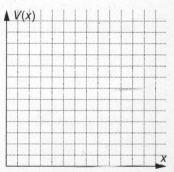

e. Approximate the value of x that produces a box with the greatest possible volume.

e. _____

Chapter 2 Test, Form B

You will need an automatic grapher for this test.

1. Let $f(x) = -3x^2 + 2x$.

   a. What is the maximum value of f?

   1. a. _____

   b. On what interval(s) is f increasing?

   b. _____

2. What is the domain and range of the function $g(x) = \log(x + 2)$?

   2. _____

3. Consider the function h graphed at the right.

   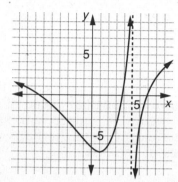

   a. Approximate the interval(s) over which h is increasing.

   3. a. _____

   b. Approximate the interval(s) over which h is decreasing.

   b. _____

   c. Approximate any relative minimum value to the nearest integer.

   c. _____

4. Consider the sequence $c_n = 2 + \left(\frac{1}{3}\right)^n$, for $n \geq 1$.

   a. Give the first three terms of c.

   4. a. _____

   b. What is $\lim\limits_{n \to \infty} c_n$?

   b. _____

5. Solve $\log_4 \frac{1}{64} = x$ for x.

   5. _____

6. Solve $\log_{27} x = \frac{4}{3}$ for x.

   6. _____

7. Rewrite $\log\left(\frac{n}{m^2}\right)$ in terms of $\log n$ and $\log m$.

   7. _____

8. Refer to the graph of the function f at the right.

   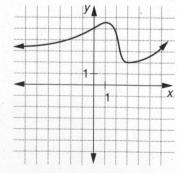

   a. Give all intervals on which f is increasing.

   8. a. _____

   b. Give all intervals on which f is decreasing.

   b. _____

   c. What appears to be the value of $\lim\limits_{x \to -\infty} f(x)$?

   c. _____

   d. For what value of x is $f(x)$ a relative minimum?

   d. _____

Precalculus and Discrete Mathematics © Scott, Foresman and Company

Chapter 2 Test, Form B (page 2)

9. If you invest $1,500 in a savings account that pays $6\frac{1}{2}\%$ interest compounded continuously, about how much will that amount become in 8 years?

9. _____

In 10 and 11, describe the end behavior of the function.

10. f, if $f(x) = .5^x$

10. _____

_____

11. g, if $g(x) = -\left(\dfrac{\sin x}{x}\right)$

11. _____

_____

12. An open box is made from a rectangular piece of steel measuring 8 inches by 10 inches. A square with sides x inches long is cut from each corner and the flaps are folded up to form the sides of the box.

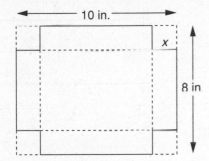 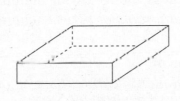

a. Express the length, l, of the base of the box as a function of x.

12. a. _____

b. Express the width, w, of the box as a function of x.

b. _____

c. Express the volume, V, of the box as a function of x.

c. _____

d. Sketch a graph of $V(x)$.

d.
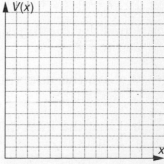

e. Approximate the value of x that produces a box with the greatest possible volume.

e. _____

Chapter 2 Test, Cumulative Form

You will need an automatic grapher for this test.

1. The table at the right gives the population density of the U.S. estimated by the census every ten years between 1790 and 1880. Let $D(x)$ be the density in year x.

Census Date	Population per Square Mile
1790	4.5
1800	6.1
1810	4.3
1820	5.5
1830	7.4
1840	9.8
1850	7.9
1860	10.6
1870	10.9
1880	14.2

   a. Describe the interval(s) where D is increasing.

   1. a. _____

   _____

   b. At which years did relative minimum values occur?

   b. _____

2. Let $p(x)$: x is prime and $x > 7$.

   a. Write $p(9)$.

   2. a. _____

   b. Is $p(9)$ true?

   b. _____

3. Use the symbol ∃ or ∀ to express the following statement.
   All positive integers are square roots of perfect squares.

   3. _____

   _____

4. Consider the following argument.

   If a person has two forms of identification, then he or she can cash a check at Smith's Department Store.
   Ed cannot cash a check at Smith's Department Store.
   ∴ *Ed does not have two forms of identification.*

   a. Write the form of this argument.

   4. a. _____

   _____

   _____

   b. Is this argument valid?

   b. _____

5. Consider the function f graphed at the right.

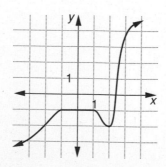

   a. Give the interval on which f is decreasing.

   5. a. _____

   b. Give the interval on which f is constant.

   b. _____

   c. Estimate the location(s) and value(s) of any relative minima.

   c. _____

   _____

Chapter 2 Test, Cumulative Form   (page 2)

6. What is the domain of g if $g(x) = \dfrac{x+2}{\sqrt{3x}}$?

6. _____

7. Let $h(x) = e^x + e^{-x}$.

   a. Sketch a graph of h.

7. **a.**

   b. What is the range of h?

b. _____

   c. Is h even, odd, or neither?

c. _____

8. Use limit notation to describe the end behavior of f when $f(x) = -x^3 + \dfrac{1}{x^2}$.

8. _____

_____

9. Write the negation of *(p or ~q)*.

9. _____

10. *Multiple choice.* Which statement(s) below is (are) equivalent to the following?

10. _____

   If a student participates in athletics, then the student must have a grade point average over 2.0.

   (a) *All students with grade point averages over 2.0 take part in athletics.*

   (b) *If a student's grade point average is above 2.0, then he or she is in athletics.*

   (c) *If a student's grade point average is 2.0 or below, then that student does not take part in athletics.*

11. Solve $\log_x 64 = 2$.

11. _____

12. The pH of a chemical solution is given by pH = -log x, where x is the concentration in moles/liter of $[H_3O^+]$ ions in the solution. Suppose the concentration of $[H_3O^+]$ ions in a particular solution is $4 \cdot 10^{-8}$ moles/liter. Find its pH.

12. _____

Chapter 2 Test, Cumulative Form   (page 3)

13. A cone-shaped cup is to be made from a paper circle with radius 10 cm. (Therefore the slant height is 10 cm.) Let x represent the radius of the base.

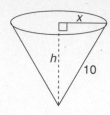

   a. Write a formula for the height, h, as a function of x.

   13. a. _____

   b. Express the volume of the cone, V, as a function of x. (Recall: volume of cone $= \frac{1}{3} \cdot$ base area $\cdot$ height)

   b. _____

   c. Sketch a graph of $V(x)$.

   c. _____

   d. Approximate the radius of the base that produces the maximum volume.

   d. _____

Precalculus and Discrete Mathematics © Scott, Foresman and Company

NAME _____

Quiz for Lessons 3-1 Through 3-3

You will need an automatic grapher for this quiz.

1. Solve. $x^{5/6} = 243$

1. _____

In 2 and 3, tell if the reasoning step is always reversible when solving an equation for x.

2. Subtracting x from both sides

2. _____

3. Dividing both sides by $(x + 2)$

3. _____

4. Let $f(x) = x^2 + 3$ and $g(x) = x - 5$.

   a. Give a simplified formula for $f \circ g$.

   4. a. _____

   b. Does $f \circ g = g \circ f$? Explain.

   b. _____

   _____

5. *True* or *false*? If $f(x) = 3x + 1$ and $g(x) = \frac{1}{3}x - 1$, then f and g are inverse functions. Justify your answer.

5. _____

   _____

6. The manufacturers of Acme Suntan Oil have three sales regions with projected sales approximated by the following functions:

   Southwest region: $f(x) = 3,000$
   Southeast region: $g(x) = 1,000 + 1,500x$
   Northern region: $h(x) = -1,000 \cos 2\pi x + 1,000$

   where $f(x)$, $g(x)$, and $h(x)$ are the number of bottles sold x years from now.

   a. How many more bottles will be sold in the Southeast region than the Northern region x years from now?

   6. a. _____

   b. Graph the total sales, $T(x)$, predicted over the next four years.

   b.

   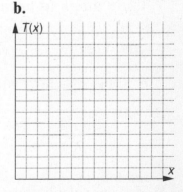

Quiz for Lessons 3-4 Through 3-7

You will need an automatic grapher for this quiz.

1. Use the graph at the right to describe all values of x for which $f(x) > g(x)$.

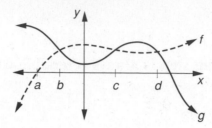

1. _____

2. **a.** How many real zeros does $f(x) = x^3 + x^2 - 8x - 3$ have?

2. **a.** _____

   b. Find an interval of length .01 that contains a positive zero of f.

   b. _____

3. Ten grams of a radioactive substance begins decaying so that after every hour, half the amount that was there the previous hour remains. At what times will there be less than .5 grams remaining? Give an exact answer.

3. _____

4. *True* or *false*? If $y^2 > 3$ on a given interval, then $\frac{1}{y^2} < \frac{1}{3}$ on that interval.

4. _____

5. Use the Test Point Method to solve $2(x - 5)(x + 1)(x + 3) > 0$.

5. _____

6. *Multiple choice.* The function $d(x) = \frac{x^2}{20} + x$ approximates the distance in feet required to stop a car that is traveling x miles per hour. At the scene of an accident, police determine from skid marks that it took 160 feet to stop a car. Which interval best describes the speed at which the car had been traveling?

   (a) 40–50 mph   (b) 50–60 mph
   (c) 60–70 mph   (d) 70–80 mph

6. _____

7. Use a graph to justify your answer to Question 6.

7.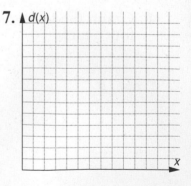

8. *True* or *false*? If $a < b$ and g is a function such that $g(a) < 0$ and $g(b) > 0$, then g has a zero between a and b. Explain your reasoning.

8. _____

   _____

9. Solve. $y^4 - 7y^2 + 12 = 0$

9. _____

Chapter 3 Test, Form A

You will need an automatic grapher for this test.

1. The graphs of f and g are sketched at the right. Use subtraction of ordinates to sketch the graph of $f - g$.

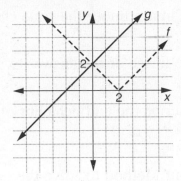

1.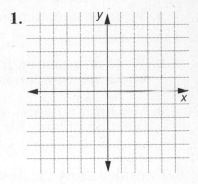

2. Let p and q be the functions defined by $p(x) = x^2 - 4$ and $q(x) = \frac{1}{x - 2}$. Find a simplified formula for $(p \cdot q)(x)$. Give the domain of $(p \cdot q)(x)$.

5.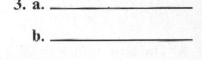

3. Suppose $P(t) = 1{,}840t$ is the altitude in meters of a small plane t minutes into its climb to cruising altitude and $R(t) = 50 - \frac{t}{100}$ is the temperature in °C at an altitude of t meters when the ground temperature is 50°C.

   a. Find a formula for $(R \circ P)(t)$.

   b. For the function $R \circ P{:}t \to (R \circ P)(t)$, what does t represent?

   c. What does $(R \circ P)(t)$ measure?

   3. a. _____

   b. _____

   c. _____

4. a. Identify the amplitude, period, and phase shift of the sine wave graphed below.

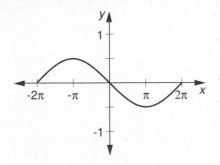

   4. a. _____

   _____

   _____

   b. Use the sine function to write an equation for the graph.

   b.

Chapter 3 Test, Form A   (page 2)

5. Consider the graph of $y = e^x$.

    a. Write an equation for its image under the scale change $S_{1/2,-3}$.

    5. **a.** _____

    b. Write an equation for the image of the answer to part **a** under the translation $T_{-1,2}$.

    b. _____

    c. Use limit notation to describe the end behavior of the function obtained in part **b.**

    c. _____

    _____

6. Consider using the Test Point Method to solve the inequality $x^3 - 10x < 3x^2$.

    a. Identify the intervals in which values must be tested.

    6. **a.** _____

    _____

    b. Solve the inequality.

    b. _____

7. *Multiple choice.* Which of the intervals listed below must contain a zero of the function f defined by $f(x) = 2x^3 + x^2 - 13x + 6$?

    7. _____

    (a) $-2 \le x \le -1$ (b) $-1 \le x \le 0$
    (c) $0 \le x \le 1$ (d) $3 \le x \le 4$

8. The equation $5^x = x^2$ has a solution between -1 and 0. Give an interval of length .1 that contains the solution.

    8. _____

9. *Multiple choice.* Identify the processes that yield reversible steps.

    9. _____

    (a) adding the same number to both sides of an equation
    (b) multiplying both sides of an equation by the same nonzero number
    (c) squaring both sides of an equation
    (d) taking the square root of both sides of an equation
    (e) dividing both sides of an equation by an expression containing a variable

In 10–13, find all real number solutions.

10. $\dfrac{5}{x + 5} < \dfrac{2}{4x - 10}$

    10. _____

11. $\left(\sqrt[5]{x}\right)^2 + 2\left(\sqrt[5]{x}\right) = -1$

    11. _____

12. $|9k + 18| < 10$

    12. _____

13. $2 \log (x + 5) = \log 64$

    13. _____

     Precalculus and Discrete Mathematics © Scott, Foresman and Company

Chapter 3 Test, Form A   (page 3)

14. The distance d (in kilometers) that can be seen from a tall building can be approximated by the equation

$$d = 112\sqrt{h}$$

where h is the height of the building (in kilometers). From what height can you see about 50 km?

14. _____

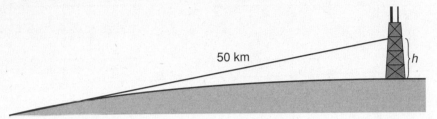

50 km

h

15. Does the function $f(x) = x^6$ have an inverse that is a function? Explain.

15. _____

_____

_____

16. Let $g(x) = \dfrac{x + 2}{x - 2}$.

    a. Show that $g(1) < 0$.

16. a. _____

    b. Show that $g(3) > 0$.

    b. _____

    c. Does g have a zero between $x = 1$ and $x = 3$? Explain your answer.

    c. _____

_____

_____

_____

17. The ideal spark plug for a particular car has a gap between electrodes that is .043 inches. The gap of an actual spark plug may vary from this ideal quantity, but the error in the gap of an acceptable spark plug must be no more than .001 inch. Write an absolute value inequality that expresses this requirement.

17. _____

_____

Chapter 3 Test, Form B

You will need an automatic grapher for this test.

1. The graphs of f and g are sketched at the right. Use subtraction of ordinates to sketch the graph of $f - g$.

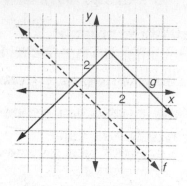

1.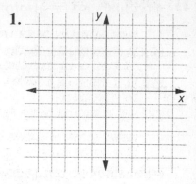

2. Let k and m be the functions defined by $k(x) = x^2 + x - 6$ and $m(x) = x + 3$. Find a simplified formula for $\left(\frac{k}{m}\right)(x)$. Give the domain of $\left(\frac{k}{m}\right)(x)$.

2. _____

_____

3. Suppose $P(x) = x - 120$ is the profit made when a television set is sold at a price of x dollars, and $n(x) = 30 - \frac{x}{10}$ is the number of televisions that customers buy in a month when the price is x dollars.

   a. Find a formula for $(P \circ n)(x)$.

   3. a. _____

   b. For the function $P \circ n: x \rightarrow (P \circ n)(x)$, what does x represent?

   b. _____

   c. What does $(P \circ n)(x)$ represent?

   c. _____

   _____

4. a. Identify the amplitude, period, and phase shift of the cosine wave graphed below.

   4. a. _____

   _____

   _____

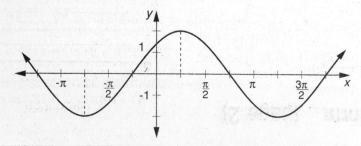

   b. Use the cosine function to write an equation for the graph.

   b. _____

Precalculus and Discrete Mathematics © Scott, Foresman and Company

Chapter 3 Test, Form B (page 2)

5. Consider the graph of $y = \ln x$.

    a. Write an equation for its image under the scale change $S_{-2,1/3}$.

    5. a. _____

    b. Write an equation for the image of the answer to part **a** under the translation $T_{2,-3}$.

    b. _____

    c. Use limit notation to describe the end behavior of the function obtained in part **b**.

    c. _____

_____

6. Consider using the Test Point Method to solve the inequality $3x^2 + 18x \le x^3$.

    a. Identify the intervals in which values must be tested.

    6. a. _____

_____

    b. Solve the inequality.

    b. _____

7. *Multiple choice.* Which of the intervals listed below must contain a zero of the function f defined by $f(x) = x^3 - 3x^2 - 10x + 23$?

    7. _____

    (a) $-2 \le x \le -1$ (b) $0 \le x \le 1$
    (c) $1 \le x \le 2$ (d) $2 \le x < 3$

8. The equation $x = 4 \ln x$ has a solution between 1 and 2. Give an interval of length .1 that contains the solution.

    8. _____

9. *Multiple choice.* Identify the process which does not necessarily yield a reversible step.

    9. _____

    (a) adding the same algebraic expression to both sides of an equation
    (b) subtracting the same algebraic expression from both sides of an equation
    (c) multiplying both sides of an equation by the same algebraic expression
    (d) taking the cube root of both sides of an equation
    (e) All of the above yield reversible steps.

In 10–13, find all real number solutions.

10. $\dfrac{3x + 4}{x - 2} > \dfrac{10}{x - 2}$

    10. _____

11. $|3y - 5| \ge 4$

    11. _____

12. $(n^2 - 1)^2 - 3(n^2 - 1) = 10$

    12. _____

13. $e^{x^2} = e^{3x - 2}$

    13. _____

Chapter 3 Test, Form B (page 3)

14. The distance d (in kilometers) that can be seen from a tall building can be approximated by the equation

14. _____

$$d = 112\sqrt{h}$$

where h is the height of the building (in kilometers). From what height can you see about 40 km?

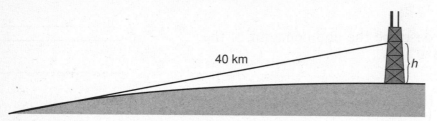

40 km

15. Does the function with equation $f(x) = (x - 1)^2$ have an inverse that is a function? Justify your answer.

15. _____

_____

_____

16. a. Find $\tan \frac{\pi}{4}$.

16. a. _____

b. Find $\tan \frac{3\pi}{4}$.

b. _____

c. Is there a solution to the equation $\tan x = 0$ between $x = \frac{\pi}{4}$ and $x = \frac{3\pi}{4}$? Justify your answer.

c. _____

_____

_____

17. A particular kind of copper wire is manufactured with an ideal diameter of .8 mm. Due to imperfections in the manufacturing process, the actual diameter may deviate from this ideal, but not by more than .005 mm. Write an absolute value inequality that expresses this requirement.

17. _____

_____

Chapter 3 Test, Cumulative Form

You will need an automatic grapher on this test.

1. Consider the function f graphed at the right.

   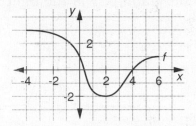

   a. Estimate the value(s) of x for which $f(x) = 1$.

   b. Identify any relative minima.

   c. What is the range of f?

   1. a. _____

   b. _____

   c. _____

2. *Multiple choice.* A solution of an equation is shown below. Which step is not reversible and therefore incorrectly contains the ⇔ symbol?

   (a) $5 + 2\sqrt{x + 3} = 19$ ⇔ $2\sqrt{x + 3} = 14$
   (b)   ⇔ $\sqrt{x + 3} = 7$
   (c)   ⇔ $x + 3 = 49$
   (d)   ⇔ $x = 46$

   2. _____

3. Show that $f(x) = \ln(x - 2)$ and $g(x) = e^x + 2$ are inverses.

   3.

4. Consider the following premises

   If a student is 16 years old and passes Driver's Education, then the student is eligible to take a driver's license test.
   Robert is not eligible to take a driver's license test.

   Deduce a valid conclusion and justify your answer.

   4. _____

   _____

   _____

   _____

5. Use the graphs of f and g below to tell whether the given value is positive, negative, or zero.

   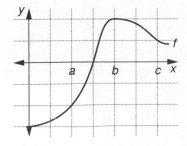
   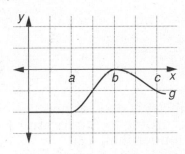

   a. $(f + g)(a)$

   b. $(f + g)(b)$

   c. $(f + g)(c)$

   5. a. _____

   b. _____

   c. _____

Chapter 3 Test, Cumulative Form (page 2)

6. The graph of $f(x) = 2^{-x^2}$ is shown at the left below. This graph is transformed into the graph of g at the right below. Give an equation for g.

6. _____

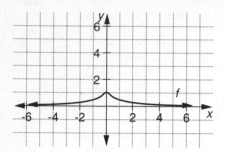
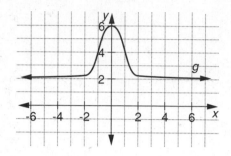

In 7–9, solve for x.

7. $\sqrt{2x - 3} = x - 3$

7. _____

8. $e^{2x} - 11e^x + 24 = 0$

8. _____

9. $|2x - 7| = x + 5$

9. _____

10. Find the range of the function g, where $g(x) = -2x^2 + 6x$, if the domain is the set of real numbers.

10. _____

11. Use the Test Point Method to solve $x^4 - 3x^3 - 28x^2 > 0$.

11. _____

12. Estimate the zeros of $f(x) = \frac{1}{3}x^3 - 3x^2 + 5x$ to the nearest tenth.

12. _____

13. What is the output signal of the logic network below if $p = 1$, $q = 1$, and $r = 0$?

13. _____

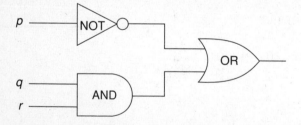

14. Does $\lim\limits_{n \to \infty} (-2)^n$ exist? If so, find it.

14. _____

15. The loudness L of a sound (in decibels) is determined from its intensity I (in watts/m²) according to the formula $L = 10 \log (I \cdot 10^{12})$. If a sound is louder than 120 decibels (the loudness of amplified rock music heard from 2 m away), what is its intensity?

15. _____

   Precalculus and Discrete Mathematics © Scott, Foresman and Company

Chapter 3 Test, Cumulative Form   (page 3)

16. A T-shirt manufacturer estimates that to sell x T-shirts it must set the price at $P(x) = 12 - \frac{x}{200}$. The company's cost for making x T-shirts is $C(x) = 1{,}000 + 4x$. Write a formula for the manufacturer's profit from selling x T-shirts as a function of x.

16. _____

17. Prove or disprove: $\forall$ *integers n and m, if m is odd, then mn is odd.*

17. _____

Comprehensive Test, Chapters 1–3

You will need an automatic grapher for this test.

1. The zeros of a function are the same as its ___?___.   1. _____
   - (a) *x*-intercepts
   - (b) *y*-intercepts
   - (c) maximum values
   - (d) minimum values

2. Which statement is equivalent to *if a < b, then $e^a < e^b$*?   2. _____
   - (a) *If a ≥ b, then $e^a ≥ e^b$.*
   - (b) *If $e^a ≥ e^b$, then a ≥ b.*
   - (c) *If $e^a < e^b$, then a < b.*
   - (d) *a < b and $e^a < e^b$.*

3. Solve. $|x - 5| < 2$ 3. _____
   - (a) *x < 3 and x < 7*
   - (b) *x < 3 or x < 7*
   - (c) *x > 3 or x < 7*
   - (d) *x > 3 and x < 7*

4. Suppose *m* is an even integer and *n* is an odd integer. What can you   4. _____
   conclude about $(m + 1)n$?
   - (a) $(m + 1)n$ is even.
   - (b) $(m + 1)n$ is odd.
   - (c) $(m + 1)n$ may be either even or odd.

5. Which interval contains a zero of $f(x) = 2x^3 - 7x^2 - 8x + 16$?   5. _____
   - (a) -2 < *x* < -1.5
   - (b) -1.5 < *x* < -1
   - (c) -1 < *x* < -.5
   - (d) -.5 < *x* < 0

6. Under which of the following conditions will the network shown   6. _____
   below generate an output value of "1"?

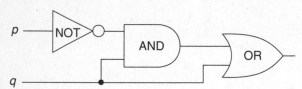

   - (a) *p* = 0, *q* = 1
   - (b) *p* = 1, *q* = 1
   - (c) both of the above
   - (d) none of the above

7. Which is the best description of the form of this argument?   7. _____

   > *If the Cougars beat the Blasters, then they are the champions.*
   > *The Cougars are not the champions.*
   > *∴ The Cougars did not beat the Blasters.*

   - (a) invalid argument
   - (b) valid argument by the Law of Detachment
   - (c) valid argument by the Law of Indirect Reasoning
   - (d) valid argument by the Law of Transitivity

8. The function *f*, where $f(x) = 3^{\cos x}$, is ___?___.   8. _____
   - (a) even
   - (b) odd
   - (c) increasing
   - (d) decreasing

Precalculus and Discrete Mathematics © Scott, Foresman and Company

Comprehensive Test, Chapters 1–3 (page 2)

9. The solution to $2 \log_5 x + \log_5 4 = \log_5 36$ is ___?___.

(a) 16   (b) $4\sqrt{2}$ (c) 12   (d) 3

9. _____

10. A botanist is breeding a new variety of miniature tree. The present generation of tree averages 34 cm in height. Each new generation is 5% shorter than the previous one. What is the least number of additional generations required to obtain trees shorter than 25 cm?

(a) 4   (b) 5   (c) 6   (d) 7

10. _____

11. What is the negation of *Today is cold and snowy*?

(a) *Today is cold or snowy.*
(b) *Today is not cold and not snowy.*
(c) *Today is cold and not snowy.*
(d) *Today is not cold or not snowy.*

11. _____

12. The functions f and g are graphed over the interval $a \leq x \leq b$ at the right. Consider the function $f + g$ over the same interval. The values of $f + g$ are ___?___.

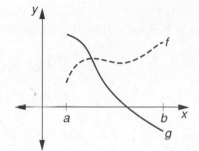

(a) always negative
(b) always positive
(c) positive for smaller values of x, then negative for larger values
(d) negative for smaller values of x, then positive for larger values

12. _____

13. The statement $\forall$ *prime numbers x, x is an integer* is equivalent to which of the following?

(a) *All prime numbers are integers.*
(b) *No prime numbers are integers.*
(c) *Some primes are integers.*
(d) *There is a prime that is an integer.*

13. _____

14. Which of these reasoning steps that might be used in solving an equation is always reversible?

(a) Taking the absolute value of each side
(b) Adding an algebraic expression to both sides
(c) Taking the square root of both sides
(d) Raising each side to the fourth power

14. _____

15. Let $f(x) = x^2$ and $g(x) = x^5$. Then $\forall$ real numbers x, ___?___.

(a) $(f \circ g)(x) = (g \circ f)(x)$ (b) $(f \circ g)(x) > (g \circ f)(x)$
(c) $(g \circ f)(x) > (f \circ g)(x)$ (d) none of these

15. _____

16. Which is the range of the function $g(x) = x^2 - 6x + 5$?

(a) set of real numbers   (b) $\{y: 1 \leq y \leq 5\}$
(c) $\{y: -4 \leq y \leq 10\}$ (d) $\{y: y \geq -4\}$

16. _____

Comprehensive Test, Chapters 1–3 (page 3)

17. Which of the following is the negation of
$\forall x$, if $x^3 - 9x = 0$, then $x = \pm 3$?

17. _____

(a) $\forall x$, if $x^3 - 9x \neq 0$, then $x \neq \pm 3$.
(b) $\forall x$, $x^3 - 9x \neq 0$ and $x \neq \pm 3$.
(c) $\exists x$ such that $x^3 - 9x = 0$ and $x \neq \pm 3$.
(d) $\exists x$ such that $x^3 - 9x \neq 0$ and $x \neq \pm 3$.

18. A function f is graphed at the right.
Find $\lim\limits_{x \to -\infty} f(x)$.

18. _____

(a) -2   (b) 1
(c) ∞ (d) $-\infty$

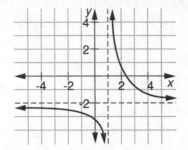

19. Find the sequence below whose limit as $n \to \infty$ is -1.

19. _____

(a) $a_n = (-1)^n$ (b) $b_n = \dfrac{1}{n} - 1$

(c) $\begin{cases} c_1 = 0 \\ c_{k+1} = c_k - 1 \end{cases}$ (d) $d_n = \dfrac{-1}{2^n}$

20. Which of the following has amplitude 2 and period π?

20. _____

(a) $f(x) = \frac{1}{2} \sin 2x$ (b) $f(x) = \frac{1}{2} \sin \frac{x}{2}$
(c) $f(x) = 2 \sin 2x$ (d) $f(x) = 2 \sin \frac{x}{2}$

21. $(x - 3)^2 (x - 7) \leq 0$ if and only if ___?___.

21. _____

(a) $x \leq 3$ (b) $3 \leq x \leq 7$
(c) $x \geq 7$ (d) $x \leq 7$

22. For x and y between 0 and π, $\cos x < \cos y$ is equivalent to ___?___.

22. _____

(a) $x < y$ (b) $x > y$

**In 23 and 24, use the graph of the function f
shown at the right.**

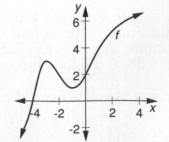

23. On which of the following intervals is f
decreasing?

23. _____

(a) $-4 \leq x \leq -3$
(b) $-3 \leq x \leq -1$
(c) $-1 \leq x \leq 0$
(d) $1 \leq x \leq 2$

24. How many solutions does the equation $f(x) = 2$ have?

24. _____

(a) 0   (b) 1   (c) 2   (d) 3

Comprehensive Test, Chapters 1–3 (page 4)

25. Which would be the last column of the truth table below?   25. _____

p	q	$\sim(p \text{ and } q)$
T	T	
T	F	
F	T	
F	F	

(a) T   (b) F   (c) T   (d) F
    F   T   F   F
    F   T   T   F
    F   T   T   T

Quiz for Lessons 4-1 Through 4-3

1. What is the degree of the product
$(x^5 - 8x^3 + 2x + 6)(x^2 - 5x - 9)$?

1. _____

2. Ten hamburgers are to be made from 3 pounds of ground beef. When figuring the weight of each hamburger, which is more appropriate to use, integer or real-number division?

2. _____

3. Mrs. Butterwort's recipe calls for cooking roast beef 27 minutes per pound. If she puts an 8-pound roast in the oven at 4:15, at how many minutes after 7:00 should she take it out?

3. _____

4. Show that $2x^3 - 50x$ is divisible by $x + 5$.

4. _____

_____

5. When n is divided by d, the quotient is 23 and the remainder is 6. Give a possible pair of values for n and d.

5. _____

6. What is the smallest nonnegative integer that satisfies $x \equiv 831 \pmod{12}$?

6. _____

7. a. List the first five terms of the sequence defined by
$$\begin{cases} a_1 & = 3 \\ a_{k+1} & = a_k + 5 \ \forall \text{ integers } k \geq 1. \end{cases}$$

7. **a.** _____

b. Use the language of congruences to write a statement that is true for all terms a_n in the sequence.

b. _____

8. The ISBN code for a book is 0-673-45260-3. Is it correct? Tell how you know.

8. _____

_____

_____

9. Prove or disprove:

If 2 is a factor of n and 5 is a factor of m, then 10 is a factor of mn.

9.

Quiz for Lessons 4-4 Through 4-6

In 1 and 2, $p(x)$ is divided by $d(x)$ to obtain a quotient $q(x)$ with remainder $r(x)$. a. What is $r(x)$? b. What is the degree of $r(x)$?

1. $p(x) = x^7 + 10x^5 + 23x^3 - 5$
$d(x) = x^2 + 3$
$q(x) = x^5 + 7x^3 + 2x$

1. a. _____

b. _____

2. $p(x) = 12x^7 + 30x^8 - 20x^6 - 8x^4$
$d(x) = 2x^4 + 5x^5$
$q(x) = 6x^3 - 4x$

2. a. _____

b. _____

3. Use long division to find the quotient and remainder when $2x^3 + 7x^2 + 9x - 8$ is divided by $x + 5$.

3. _____

_____

4. Given that $x - 4$ is a factor of $x^3 - 2x^2 - 23x + 60$, find the other two factors.

4. _____

5. Write $6x^4 - 3x^3 + 5x^2 + 6x$ in nested form.

5. _____

6. Refer to the synthetic division of $p(x)$ by $d(x)$ shown below.

```
-5| 3    10   -24    0   -25
       -15    25   -5    25
   ─────────────────────────
    3    -5     1   -5     0
```

a. What is $d(x)$?

6. a. _____

b. What is the quotient?

b. _____

c. What is the remainder?

c. _____

7. Bill solved $2x^3 + 6x^2 - 36x - 80 = 0$ and got $x = -5$, $x = -2$, $x = 3$, or $x = 4$. How can you tell that Bill is wrong?

7. _____

_____

8. Use synthetic division to find $p(3)$ when $p(x) = 8x^3 - 5x^2 + 4x + 2$.

8. _____

Chapter 4 Test, Form A

1. A tea manufacturer packages 24 tea bags in every box. Suppose 10,000 tea bags are manufactured.

   a. How many boxes are filled?

   b. How many tea bags remain unboxed?

   c. Write an equation in the form of the Quotient-Remainder Theorem to describe the situation.

   1. a. _____

   b. _____

   c. _____

2. Suppose that the integer n divided by the integer d yields a quotient of 3 and a remainder of 4. Give possible values of n and d.

   2. _____

3. Show that $3x + 1$ is a factor of $3x^2 + 22x + 7$.

   3. _____

4. Use long division to find the quotient $q(x)$ and the remainder $r(x)$ when $p(x) = -6x^4 + 18x^3 - x^2 + 27x + 10$ is divided by $d(x) = 2x^2 + 3$.

   4. _____

   _____

5. *True* or *false*? The graph at the right could be the graph of a sixth-degree polynomial function. Justify your answer.

   5. _____

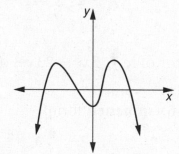

In 6 and 7, prove the given statement or disprove it by giving a counterexample.

6. ∀ integers n, $n^3 + 3n^2 + 2n$ is divisible by 3. (Hint: Factor out n.)

   6.

Precalculus and Discrete Mathematics © Scott, Foresman and Company

Chapter 4 Test, Form A (page 2)

7. ∀ integers a, b, and c, if a divides $b + c$, then a divides b
   or a divides c.

   7. _____

8. Write the base-10 representation of 11011_2.

   8. _____

9. Add $10011_2 + 1010_2$. Give your answer in base 2.

   9. _____

10. Fill in the blank with the smallest positive integer
    solution.

    $1{,}034 \equiv \underline{\ ?\ } \pmod 5$.

    10. _____

11. Suppose 11 is a factor of $x - 4$. Express this fact using
    the language of congruences.

    11. _____

12. Find the last three digits of 9^{13}.

    12. _____

13. Give the standard prime factorization of 2,040.

    13. _____

14. Give the prime factorization of $3x^4 - 3x^2 - 36$ over the
    real numbers.

    14. _____

15. Given that -4 is a solution of $6x^3 + 17x^2 - 33x - 20 = 0$,
    find the other solutions.

    15. _____

16. Use synthetic division to find $p(-7)$ if
    $p(x) = 2x^3 + 19x^2 + 31x - 25$.

    16. _____

17. Consider the statement *There is no smallest negative
    integer.*

    a. To write a proof by contradiction, with what
       assumption would you start?

       17. a. _____

       _____

       _____

    b. Complete the proof.

       b.

Chapter 4 Test, Form B

1. A baker packages hotdog buns eight to a bag. Suppose 2,500 buns have been produced.

   a. How many bags are filled?

   1. a. _____

   b. How many buns remain unpackaged?

   b. _____

   c. Write an equation in the form of the Quotient-Remainder Theorem to describe the situation.

   c. _____

2. Suppose that the integer n divided by the integer d yields a quotient of 4 and a remainder of 3. Give possible values of n and d.

   2. _____

3. Show that $4x + 2$ is a factor of $4x^2 + 30x + 14$.

   3. _____

4. Use long division to find the quotient $q(x)$ and the remainder $r(x)$ when $p(x) = 6x^4 - 15x^3 - 17x^2 - 9x - 13$ is divided by $d(x) = 3x^2 + 2$.

   4. _____

   _____

5. *True* or *false*? The graph at the right could be the graph of a fourth-degree polynomial function. Justify your answer.

   5. _____

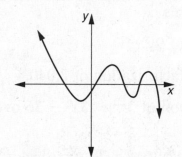

In 6 and 7, prove the given statement or disprove it by giving a counterexample.

6. ∀ integers n, $n^3 - n$ is divisible by 4. (Hint: Factor out n.)

   6.

 Precalculus and Discrete Mathematics © Scott, Foresman and Company

Chapter 4 Test, Form B   (page 2)

7. ∀ integers a, b, and c, if a divides b and a divides c, then a divides $b - c$.

7.

8. Write the base-10 representation of 101101_2.

8. _____

9. Add $11010_2 + 1011_2$. Give your answer in base 2.

9. _____

10. Fill in the blank with the smallest positive integer solution.

$$2{,}419 \equiv \underline{\quad ? \quad} \ (\text{mod } 12)$$

10. _____

11. Suppose 13 is a factor of $x - 3$. Express this fact using the language of congruences.

11. _____

12. Find the last three digits of 12^{15}.

12. _____

13. Give the standard prime factorization of 4,820.

13. _____

14. Give the prime factorization of $x^4 + 10x^2 - 9$ over the real numbers.

14. _____

15. Given that 2 is a solution of $2x^3 + 5x^2 - 23x + 10 = 0$, find the other solutions.

15. _____

16. Use synthetic division to find $p(4)$ if $p(x) = 8x^4 + 12x^2 - 7x + 9$.

16. _____

17. Consider the statement *There is no largest integer which is divisible by 3.*

  a. To write a proof by contradiction, with what assumption would you start?

  17. a. _____

  _____

  _____

  b. Complete the proof.

  b.

Chapter 4 Test, Cumulative Form

You will need an automatic grapher on this test.

1. When $p(x)$ is divided by $x^3 - 3x^2 + 5x$ the quotient is $2x + 1$ and the remainder is 7. What is $p(x)$?

1. _____

2. If $p(x)$ and $q(x)$ are polynomials such that $p(x) = q(x)(x + 2) + 3$, then $p(\underline{\quad a. \quad}) = \underline{\quad b. \quad}$.

2. a. _____

   b. _____

3. Solve $\ln (x^2 - 16) = \ln (6x)$.

3. _____

4. Write the negation of the statement $\forall x, x + 1 < x + 2$ *and* $x \neq -x$.

4. _____

_____

5. A case of soda consists of 24 cans.

  a. How many cases of soda could fit in a storage area which holds 500 cans?

5. a. _____

  b. How many separate cans would there still be room for?

   b. _____

  c. Write an equation in the form of the Quotient-Remainder Theorem to describe the situation.

   c. _____

6. If $p(x) = 4x^2 - 5x + 10$ and $c = 2.2$, use synthetic division to find $p(c)$.

6. _____

7. Suppose that the value of the dollar is shrinking 5% per year. How much will one dollar be worth in 25 years?

7. _____

8. In a class of 24 children, students count off "1, 2, 3, 4, 5, 6, 1, 2, 3, ..." to form six kickball teams. Which students are on the same team as student #14?

8. _____

                     Precalculus and Discrete Mathematics © Scott, Foresman and Company

Chapter 4 Test, Cumulative Form   (page 2)

9. The graph of $f(x) = |x - 2|$ is transformed to the
congruent graph of g shown below. Write a formula for g.

9. _____

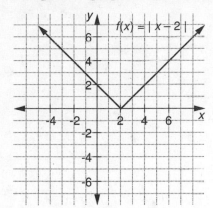
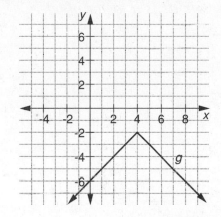

10. Find the quotient and remainder when $x^4 - 16$ is divided
by $x + 2$.

10. _____
_____

11. Identify any relative maxima and minima of
$g(x) = x^3 - 4x^2 - 7x + 10$.

11. _____
_____

12. Write the base-10 representation of 110100_2.

12. _____

13. If $f(x) = x + \frac{1}{x}$ and $g(x) = x - \frac{2}{x}$, write a formula for
$(f \cdot g)(x)$.

13. _____

14. Describe the end behavior of the sine function.

14. _____
_____

15. *True* or *false*? $18 \equiv 53 \pmod 7$. Justify your answer.

15. _____
_____
_____

16. Let $f(x) = x^{3/4} + 5$ and $g(x) = (x - 5)^{4/3}$. Show that f and
g are inverses.

16.

17. Complete the truth table for *p and (~p or q)*.

17.

p	q	
T	T	
T	F	
F	T	
F	F	

18. Prove or disprove:

If a, b, c, and d are integers such that a is a factor of b and c is a factor of d, then ac is a factor of bd.

18.

19. Consider the statement *There is no largest integer that can be written as an integer power of 10.*

a. To prove this using proof by contradiction, with what statement would you begin?

19. a. _____

_____

_____

_____

b. Complete the proof.

b.

Quiz for Lessons 5-1 Through 5-3

1. Rationalize the denominator. $\dfrac{\sqrt{2}}{5\sqrt{2} - 1}$

1. _____

2. Simplify $\dfrac{x^2 + x}{x^2 + 2x} \cdot \dfrac{x + 2}{x^2 - 4x - 5}$. State the restrictions on x.

2. _____

3. *Multiple choice.* Let $p(x)$ be the statement x *is an irrational number and* $5 < x < 7$. Which of the following is true?

   (a) $p(\sqrt{6})$ (b) $p(\sqrt{36})$ (c) $p(2\pi)$ (d) $p(\sqrt{3} \cdot \sqrt{36})$

3 _____

4. Bill can paint a house in n days and Nancy can do it in $n + 3$ days. Assume Bill works for 2 days and Nancy works for 1 day.

   a. What fraction of the house does Bill paint?

   4. a. _____

   b. What fraction of the house does Nancy paint?

   b. _____

   c. What fraction do they both paint together?

   c. _____

5. Give a value of x for which $\dfrac{17}{x^2 + 1}$ is irrational.

5. _____

6. a. Sketch a graph of the function $f(x) = -\dfrac{1}{x^3}$.

   6. a.

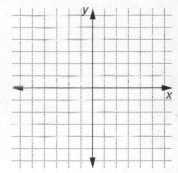

   b. Describe the end behavior of f using limit notation.

   b. _____

   c. Describe the behavior of f near any vertical asymptotes using limit notation.

   c. _____

7. Prove that $\sqrt{19}$ is irrational.

7.

Quiz for Lessons 5-4 Through 5-6

You will need an automatic grapher for this quiz.

1. Give an example of a function that is not a rational function.

1. _____

2. Consider the function $g(x) = \dfrac{x + 2}{x^2 + 8x + 12}$.

   a. Use limit notation to describe the end behavior.

   2. a. _____

   b. Use limit notation to describe the behavior near any vertical asymptote(s).

   b. _____

   c. Classify all discontinuities as essential or removable.

   c. _____

3. The graph of the function h, shown at the right, has a hole in it at $x = 3$. Write a formula for h.

   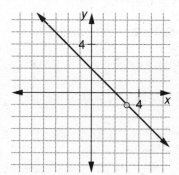

   3. _____

4. Graph $f(x) = \dfrac{x^3 + 3}{x^2 - 1}$. Show any asymptotes or holes.

   4.

   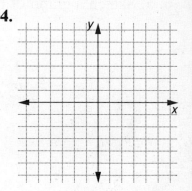

5. Refer to the graph of g at right.

   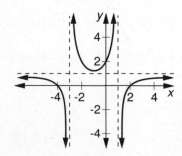

   a. Write the equation(s) of any horizontal asymptote(s).

   5. a. _____

   b. What is $\lim\limits_{x \to -3^+} g(x)$?

   b. _____

6. Find $\sec \dfrac{\pi}{6}$.

   6. _____

7. Let $f(x) = \csc x$.

   a. For what values of x is f undefined?

   7. a. _____

   b. Are the discontinuities of f at these values essential or removable?

   b. _____

Chapter 5 Test, Form A

You will need an automatic grapher for this test.

In 1 and 2, a. simplify and b. state any restrictions on the variables.

1. $\dfrac{3x + 4}{x + 6} - \dfrac{2x}{x + 1}$

1. a. _____

   b. _____

2. $\dfrac{3(x + 5)}{(x + 7)(x - 9)} \div \dfrac{2(x + 7)}{x - 9}$

2. a. _____

   b. _____

3. Let $f(x) = 5\sqrt{x} + 3$.

   a. *True* or *false?* f is a rational function.

   b. Give a value of x such that $f(x)$ is a rational number.

   c. Give a value of x such that $f(x)$ is an irrational number.

3. a. _____

   b. _____

   c. _____

4. Prove that $\sqrt{5}$ is irrational.

4.

5. The Doppler effect is the perceived change in the pitch of a sound emitted by an object as that object moves relative to the observer. Suppose a train is moving away from an individual with a velocity v and its whistle emits a sound with frequency f. Then if s is the speed of sound, the observer hears the whistle with a frequency h given by

$$h = \dfrac{f}{1 + \dfrac{v}{s}}.$$

   Find a simple fraction that expresses h.

5. _____

6. Rational the denominator. $\dfrac{2\sqrt{5}}{\sqrt{5} - 6}$

6. _____

7. A function g is defined by the rule $g(x) = \frac{4x - 1}{3x + 2}$.

   a. Identify the domain of g.   7. a. _____

   b. Identify any discontinuities as essential or removable.   b. _____

   c. Find equations for any horizontal and vertical   c. _____
      asymptotes.

   d. Find the x- and y-intercepts.   d. _____

   e. Sketch a graph of g.   e.

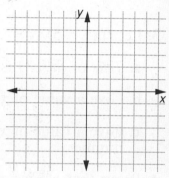

8. Solve for z: $\frac{3}{z + 1} - \frac{2z}{z - 5} = \frac{7}{3}$.   8. _____

9. Use limit notation to express the following sentence.   9. _____

   As x approaches 4 from the right, $\frac{1}{x - 4}$ approaches positive infinity.

10. Refer to the graph of f at the
    right.

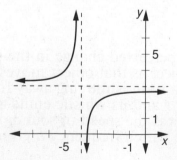

    a. Use limit notation to describe   10. a. _____
       the behavior of f near any
       vertical asymptote(s).   _____

    b. Use limit notation to describe   b. _____
       the end behavior of f.
                                                                     _____

11. Find the equation of the oblique asymptote of   11. _____
    $g(x) = \frac{x^3 + 4x^2 - 4x + 10}{x^2 + x - 1}$.

Precalculus and Discrete Mathematics © Scott, Foresman and Company

12. Give the exact value of cot $\frac{7\pi}{6}$.

12. _____

13. Use the triangle at the right to find an expression for csc θ.

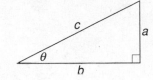

13. _____

14. Graph $f(x) = \csc x$ for $0 \le x \le 2\pi$.

14.

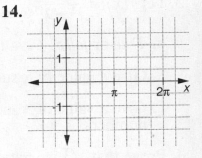

15. *True* or *false*? The quotient of any two irrational numbers is always irrational. Justify your answer.

15. _____

Chapter 5 Test, Form B

You will need an automatic grapher for this test.

In 1 and 2, a. simplify, and b. state any restrictions on the variables.

1. $\dfrac{2}{x-5} + \dfrac{3}{x^2 - 25}$

1. a. _____

   b. _____

2. $\dfrac{5(x+2)}{(x+3)(x-5)} \div \dfrac{2(x+3)}{(x-5)}$

2. a. _____

   b. _____

3. Let $f(x) = \dfrac{3}{x^2 + 2}$.

   a. *True* or *false?* f is a rational function.

3. a. _____

   b. Give a value of x such that $f(x)$ is a rational number.

   b. _____

   c. Give a value of x such that $f(x)$ is an irrational number.

   c. _____

4. Prove that $\sqrt{3}$ is irrational.

4.

5. If the resistors in the electrical circuit below have resistances R_1, R_2, and R_3, then the total resistance R is given by

5. _____

$$R = \dfrac{1}{\dfrac{1}{R_1} + \dfrac{1}{R_2}} + R_3.$$

Find a single simplified fraction for R.

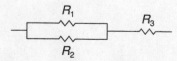

6. Rationalize the denominator. $\dfrac{3\sqrt{2}}{2\sqrt{3} + 3}$

6. _____

Precalculus and Discrete Mathematics © Scott, Foresman and Company

7. A function g is defined by the rule $g(x) = \dfrac{2x - 3}{4x + 1}$.

    a. Identify the domain of g.

    b. Identify any discontinuities as essential or removable.

    c. Find equations for any horizontal and vertical asymptotes.

    d. Find the x- and y-intercepts.

    e. Sketch a graph of g.

7. **a.** _____

    b. _____

    c. _____

    d. _____

    e.

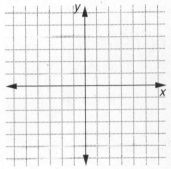

8. Solve for z. $\dfrac{1}{2z - 2} + \dfrac{3z}{z + 1} = \dfrac{5}{2}$

8. _____

9. Use limit notation to express the following sentence.

    As x approaches -2 from the left, $\dfrac{1}{(x + 2)^2}$ approaches positive infinity.

9. _____

10. Refer to the graph of f at the right.

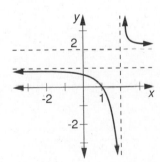

    a. Use limit notation to describe the behavior of f near any vertical asymptote(s).

    b. Use limit notation to describe the end behavior of f.

10. **a.** _____

    _____

    b. _____

    _____

11. Find the equation of the oblique asymptote of
$g(x) = \dfrac{3x^3 - 9x^2 + 7x + 13}{x^2 + 1}$.

11. _____

Chapter 5 Test, Form B   (page 3)

12. Give us the exact value of csc $\frac{2\pi}{3}$.

12. _____

13. Use the triangle at the right to find an expression for sec θ.

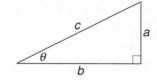

13. _____

14. Graph $f(x) = \sec x$ for $0 \le x \le 2\pi$.

14.
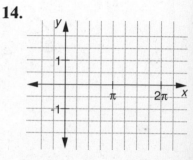

15. *True* or *false*? The product of an irrational number and a real number is an irrational number. Justify your answer.

15. _____

Precalculus and Discrete Mathematics © Scott, Foresman and Company

Chapter 5 Test, Cumulative Form

You will need an automatic grapher for this test.

1. Refer to the graph of f at the right.

   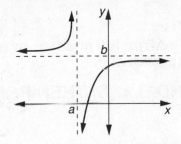

   a. What is $\lim\limits_{x \to a^-} f(x)$?

   b. Write the equation of the horizontal asymptote.

   1. a. _____

   b. _____

2. How is the graph of $g(x) = 2x^2$ different from the graph of $h(x) = \frac{2x^3 - 14x^2}{x - 7}$?

   2. _____

   _____

   _____

3. What is $\lim\limits_{x \to 5^+} \frac{x^2}{x^2 - 9x + 20}$?

   3. _____

4. Given that $4x + 7$ is a factor of $8x^3 - 34x^2 - 44x + 70$, factor $8x^3 - 34x^2 - 44x + 70$ completely.

   4. _____

5. If $\frac{\pi}{2} < \theta < \pi$ and $\sin \theta = .4$, approximate $\cot \theta$.

   5. _____

6. Is $\tan \pi$ rational or irrational?

   6. _____

7. Simplify $\frac{x^2 + x + 1}{x^2 + 3x - 10} - \frac{x}{x + 5}$. State any restrictions on x.

   7. _____

8. Rationalize the denominator. $\frac{-2\sqrt{3}}{4 - \sqrt{3}}$

   8. _____

9. Synthetic division is used to divide $p(x)$ by $q(x)$ as shown at the right. Write the corresponding equation in the form $p(x) = d(x) \cdot q + r(x)$.

$$\begin{array}{r|rrrr} 2| & 3 & -8 & 5 & 9 \\ & & 6 & -4 & 2 \\ \hline & 3 & -2 & 1 & 11 \end{array}$$

   9. _____

   _____

10. A camper can paddle a canoe at a speed of 5 mph in still water. She can travel 20 miles downstream on Poplar River in the same amount of time that it takes her to go 5 miles upstream. How fast is the current in Poplar River?

    10. _____

11. Suppose $p(x)$ is a fourth-degree polynomial.

    a. What is the greatest number of real zeros $p(x)$ can have?

    11. a. _____

    b. What is the least number of real zeros $p(x)$ can have?

    b. _____

Chapter 5 Test, Cumulative Form (page 2)

12. Let $f(x) = \frac{5}{x+2}$ and $g(x) = \frac{1}{x}$. Write a simplified
expression for $(f \circ g)(x)$.

12. _____

13. Use De Morgan's Laws to rewrite the negation in the
following line of a computer program.

13. _____

    50   IF NOT (A < B AND B < C) THEN PRINT
           "ERROR"

14. Approximate the value of any relative minima of
$h(x) = \frac{2x^3 - x}{x - 1}$ to the nearest tenth.

14. _____

_____

15. When 428 is divided by 11, the quotient is q and the
remainder is r. Find the values of q and r that satisfy the
Quotient-Remainder Theorem.

15. _____

16. Solve. $|2x - 37| \geq 105$

16. _____

17. Prove that $\sqrt{17}$ is irrational.

17. _____

Precalculus and Discrete Mathematics © Scott, Foresman and Company

Quiz for Lessons 6-1 Through 6-3

1. a. Use an automatic grapher. Does $\frac{\cot x}{\sec x} = \frac{1}{\sin x} - \sin x$ appear to be an identity?

b. If so, give the apparent domain. If not, illustrate with a counterexample.

2. Use a counterexample to show that the equation $2 \sin x = \sin 2x$ is *not* an identity.

3. If $\frac{3\pi}{2} < x < 2\pi$ and $\cos x = \frac{1}{3}$, find the exact value of $\tan x$.

4. Express $\cos \frac{7\pi}{12}$ in terms of rational numbers and radicals.

1. a. _____

b. _____

3. _____

4. _____

In 5 and 6, prove the identity.

5. $\frac{1}{\sin x \cos x} - \cot x = \tan x$

6. $\frac{\cos 5x}{\sin x} - \frac{\sin 5x}{\cos x} = \frac{\cos 6x}{\sin x \cos x}$
(Hint: Express $6x$ as $5x + x$.)

Quiz for Lessons 6-4 Through 6-6

In 1–3, write a formula for the given expression.

1. $\cos(\alpha + \beta)$

2. $\tan(a - b)$

3. $\sin 2x$

1. _____

2. _____

3. _____

4. Find an identity for $\sin\left(x + \frac{\pi}{6}\right)$.

4. _____

5. If $\pi < x < \frac{3\pi}{2}$ and $\cos x = -\frac{8}{17}$, find the exact value of $\sin 2x$.

5. _____

6. Find the exact value of $\cos(\tan^{-1}(-\sqrt{3}))$.

6. _____

7. Prove the identity $\tan\theta = \frac{\sin 2\theta}{1 + \cos 2\theta}$ and give its domain.

7. _____

8. A brace is to be positioned between two beams as shown at the right. Express θ in terms of a and b.

8. _____

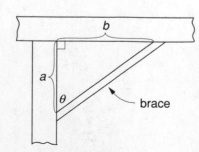

brace

Chapter 6 Test, Form A

1. Suppose $\frac{3\pi}{2} < \theta < 2\pi$ and $\sin \theta = -\frac{2}{5}$. Find the exact value of $\cos \theta$.

1. _____

In 2 and 3, prove the identity and give its domain.

2. $\dfrac{\cos (x + y)}{\sin x \sin y} + 1 = \cot x \cot y$

2. _____

3. $4 \sin x \cos x + \sin 4x = 8 \sin x \cos^3 x$

3. _____

4. *Multiple choice.* Which of the following is equivalent to $\cos \frac{\pi}{3}$?

4. _____

   (a) $2 \sin \frac{\pi}{6} \cos \frac{\pi}{6}$ (b) $2 \cos^2 \frac{\pi}{6} + 1$

   (c) $\cos^2 \frac{\pi}{6} - \sin^2 \frac{\pi}{6}$ (d) $1 - 2 \cos^2 \frac{\pi}{6}$

5. Prove or disprove:
   $\forall$ *real numbers* x, $\cos \left(x - \frac{\pi}{2}\right) = \sin (-x)$.

5.

6. Express $\cos \frac{3\pi}{8}$ in terms of rational numbers and radicals.

6. _____

Chapter 6 Test, Form A   (page 2)

7. a. Use an automatic grapher. Sketch a graph of the function $y = \sin 2x - (\sin x + \cos x)^2$.

7. a.

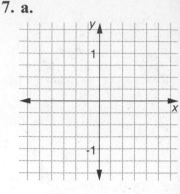

b. Based on the graph in part **a**, conjecture an identity.

b. _____

8. If $0 \le x < \frac{\pi}{2}$, $\cos x = \frac{12}{13}$, $0 \le y < \frac{\pi}{2}$, and $\sin y = \frac{3}{5}$, find $\sin (x + y)$.

8. _____

9. Describe all real numbers that are solutions of $\cos^2 x = \frac{1}{4}$.

9. _____

10. a. In the interval $0 \le x \le \pi$, determine where $\sin x = \sin 2x$.

10. a. _____

b. On the interval $0 \le x \le \pi$, determine where $\sin x \ge \sin 2x$.

b. _____

In 11 and 12, give an exact value.

11. $\tan \left(\sin^{-1} \frac{1}{2} \right)$

11. _____

12. $\sin^{-1} \left(\sin \frac{3\pi}{4} \right)$

12. _____

13. The punter on a football team wants to kick a 180-foot punt. Ignoring spin, the range of the kick is approximated by $R = \frac{v_0^2}{32} \sin 2\theta$, where v_0 is the initial velocity of the ball. At what angle should the punter kick the ball if he kicks it with an initial velocity of 80 ft/sec?

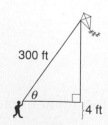

180 ft

13. _____

14. A child 4 feet tall flies a kite on a 300 foot string. If the string is straight, find a formula for the angle θ that the string makes with the horizontal as a function of the altitude of the kite above the ground.

300 ft

θ

4 ft

14. _____

Precalculus and Discrete Mathematics © Scott, Foresman and Company

Chapter 6 Test, Form B

1. Suppose $\pi < \theta < \frac{3\pi}{2}$ and $\sin \theta = -\frac{4}{5}$. Find the exact value of $\cos \theta$.

1. _____

In 2 and 3, prove the identity and give its domain.

2. $\dfrac{\sin (x - y)}{\sin x \cos y} - 1 = -\cot x \tan y$

2. _____

3. $(\cot^2 x + 1)(1 - \cos 2x) = 2$

3. _____

4. *Multiple choice.* Which of the following is equivalent to $\sin \frac{\pi}{3}$?

4. _____

   (a) $2 \sin \frac{\pi}{6} \cos \frac{\pi}{6}$ (b) $\cos^2 \frac{\pi}{3} + \sin^2 \frac{\pi}{3}$

   (c) $2 \cos^2 \frac{\pi}{3}$ (d) $2 \cos^2 \frac{\pi}{3} - 1$

5. Prove or disprove:
    ∀ real numbers x, $\sin \left(x + \frac{\pi}{2}\right) = -\cos x$.

5. _____

6. Express $\sin \frac{\pi}{8}$ in terms of rational numbers and radicals.

6. _____

Chapter 6 Test, Form B (page 2)

7. a. Use an automatic grapher. Sketch a graph of the function $y = \cos 2x - 2\cos^2 x$.

7. a.
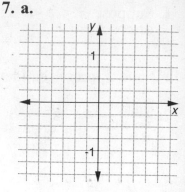

b. Based on the graph in part **a**, conjecture an identity.

b. _____

8. If $0 \le x < \frac{\pi}{2}$, $\cos x = \frac{5}{6}$, $0 \le y < \frac{\pi}{2}$, and $\sin y = \frac{7}{8}$, find $\sin (x + y)$.

8. _____

9. Describe all real numbers that are solutions of $\sin^2 x = \frac{1}{4}$.

9. _____

10. a. In the interval $0 \le x \le \pi$, determine where $\cos x = \cos 2x$.

10. a. _____

b. _____

b. On the interval $0 \le x \le \pi$, determine where $\cos x \ge \cos 2x$.

In 11 and 12, give an exact value.

11. $\cos \left(\cos^{-1} \frac{\sqrt{2}}{2} \right)$

11. _____

12. $\tan \left(\cos^{-1} \left(\frac{-2}{3} \right) \right)$

12. _____

13. The punter on a football team wants to kick a 150-foot punt. Ignoring spin, the range of the kick is approximated by $R = \frac{v_0^2}{32} \sin 2\theta$, where v_0 is the initial velocity of the ball. At what angle should the punter kick the ball if he kicks it with an initial velocity of 85 ft/sec?

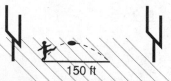

13. _____

14. Suppose the trailer on a truck is 3 ft off the ground so that a ramp must be used to load and unload it. Express the angle the ramp makes with the ground in terms of the length, l, of the ramp.

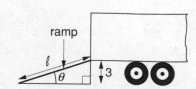

14. _____

Precalculus and Discrete Mathematics © Scott, Foresman and Company

Chapter 6 Test, Cumulative Form

You will need an automatic grapher on this test.

1. Is the equation $\frac{\cos x}{1 - \sin x} - \tan x = \cos x$ an identity? If so, give the domain. If not, give a counterexample.

1. _____

2. Express $\sin \frac{7\pi}{8}$ in terms of rational numbers and radicals.

2. _____

3. Use limit notation to describe the behavior of g, if $g(x) = \frac{x^3}{x^4 - 1}$, as x approaches 1 from the right.

3. _____

4. Prove an identity for $\cos (\pi + x)$.

4.

5. A highway engineer has determined experimentally that when traffic is heavy and moving at m miles per hour, approximately N cars pass an observation point each minute, where $N = \dfrac{88m}{20 + \frac{m^2}{20}}$. Write a simplified expression for N.

5. _____

6. Write a formula for a function with essential discontinuities at $x = -3$ and $x = 5$.

6. _____

7. Give an exact value of $\tan \left(\sin^{-1} \frac{\sqrt{3}}{2} \right)$.

7. _____

8. **a.** Find all real numbers that are solutions of $2 \sin^2 x - \sin x = 0$.

8. **a.** _____

   b. Solve $2 \sin^2 x - \sin x > 0$ for $0 \leq x \leq 2\pi$.

   b. _____

9. Express the sum in base-2 notation: 11001_2
   $+ \ 10111_2$

9. _____

NAME _____

Chapter 6 Test, Cumulative Form   (page 2)

10. If $\tan a = \frac{1}{5}$ and $\tan b = 2$, find the exact value of   **10.** _____
$\tan (a + b)$.

11. Prove: *Any perfect square is either a multiple of 3 or 1*   **11.**
more than a multiple of 3. (Hint: Any integer can be
written in the form $3k$, $3k + 1$, or $3k + 2$, where k is an
integer.)

12. Use a graph to approximate the solution of $2^t > 5t$ to the   **12.** _____
nearest tenth.

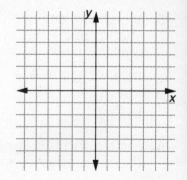

13. Prove the identity $\frac{1 + \tan x}{1 + \cot x} = \tan x$ and give the domain.   **13.** _____

14. If $f(x) = x - 3$ and $g(x) = \frac{5}{x^2 - 9}$, give a simplified   **14.** _____
formula for $(f \cdot g)(x)$.

                                      Precalculus and Discrete Mathematics © Scott, Foresman and Company

Chapter 6 Test, Cumulative Form   (page 3)

15. A piston connected to a
wheel causes the wheel to
turn as shown at the right.
A 15 cm rod connects the
piston to the wheel at
point A, and the radius of
the wheel is 8 cm. Let d be
the perpendicular distance
between point A and the
line l.

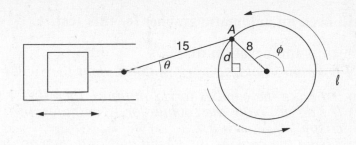

a. Find a formula for the angle θ shown in the diagram as   **10. a.** _____
a function of d.

b. Find an expression for d in terms of the angle ϕ shown   **b.** _____
in the diagram, where ϕ is the angle of rotation of
point A.

c. Use the answers from parts **a** and **b** to express the angle   **c.** _____
θ as a function of the angle ϕ.

Comprehensive Test, Chapters 1-6

You will need an automatic grapher for this test.

1. Which is the negation of   1. _____

   If I bake the cookies for 12 minutes, then they will be crispy.

   (a) *If I bake the cookies for 12 minutes, then they will not be crispy.*
   (b) *If I do not bake the cookies for 12 minutes, then they will not be crispy.*
   (c) *I bake the cookies for 12 minutes and they are not crispy.*
   (d) *I do not bake the cookies for 12 minutes and they are not crispy.*

2. Find the solution to the inequality $2 \sin^2 x + \sin x < 1$ over the   2. _____
   interval $0 \le x \le 2\pi$.

   (a) $0 < x < \frac{\pi}{6}$ or $\frac{5\pi}{6} < x < \frac{3\pi}{2}$

   (b) $\frac{\pi}{6} < x < \frac{5\pi}{6}$ or $\frac{3\pi}{2} < x < 2\pi$

   (c) $0 < x < \frac{\pi}{6}$ or $\frac{5\pi}{6} < x < 2\pi$

   (d) $0 < x < \frac{\pi}{6}$ or $\frac{5\pi}{6} < x < \frac{3\pi}{2}$ or $\frac{3\pi}{2} < x < 2\pi$

3. Which word describes the sequence defined by $S_n = \sin n\pi$ where n 3. _____
   is a positive integer?

   (a) increasing   (b) decreasing
   (c) alternating   (d) constant

4. Which value for n does *not* make the congruence $n \equiv 7 \pmod 4$ true? 4. _____

   (a) -21   (b) -5   (c) 71   (d) 129

5. Simplify $\frac{x + 5}{x - 1} - \frac{x^2 + 2}{x^2 + 2x - 3}$.   5. _____

   (a) $\frac{8x + 17}{x^2 + 2x - 3}$ (b) $\frac{8x + 13}{x^2 + 2x - 3}$

   (c) $\frac{x^2 + x + 3}{x^2 + 2x - 3}$ (d) $\frac{17}{x^2 + 2x - 3}$

6. Which of the following is equivalent to $\csc x - \cos x \cot x$?   6. _____

   (a) $\cos x$ (b) $\sin x$ (c) $\tan x$ (d) 1

7. Which of the following is equivalent to   7. _____
   $(x - 3)(x - 10)(x - 12) \ge 0$?

   (a) $x \le 3$ or $10 \le x \le 12$ (b) $3 \le x \le 10$ or $x \ge 12$
   (c) $x \le 3$ or $x \ge 12$ (d) $3 \le x \le 12$

Comprehensive Test, Chapters 1–6 (page 2)

8. Which of the following is *not* a universal statement?　　　　　**8.** _____

(a) All cows eat grass.
(b) ∀ real numbers x, $x^2 < x^4$
(c) Each of the bands did a good job.
(d) ∃ an integer x such that x is a factor of n.

9. One factor of $2x^3 + 7x^2 - 77x - 40$ is $x - 5$. Which of the following　　**9.** _____
is also a factor?

(a) $2x + 1$　　　　(b) $2x - 1$　　　　(c) $2x - 8$　　　　(d) $2x + 8$

10. To use proof by contradiction to prove *If a prime p is a factor of n^2,*　　**10.** _____
then p is a factor of n, with which assumption do you begin?

(a) p is not a factor of n.
(b) If p is not a factor of n^2, then p is not a factor of n.
(c) If p is a factor of n^2, then p is not a factor of n.
(d) p is a factor of n^2 and p is not a factor of n.

11. Which is the domain of $f(x) = \dfrac{x-5}{\sqrt{x-2}}$?　　　　**11.** _____

(a) the set of all real numbers
(b) the set of all real numbers greater than 2
(c) the set of all real numbers except 2
(d) the set of all real numbers except 5

12. Which value is a counterexample that shows $2\sin^2 x + \cos x = 1$ is　　**12.** _____
not an identity?

(a) 2π　　　　(b) $\dfrac{2\pi}{3}$　　　　(c) $\dfrac{4\pi}{3}$　　　　(d) π

13. If f is an odd function, which of the following is true?　　　　**13.** _____

(a) ∀ real numbers x, $f(-x) = -f(x)$
(b) ∀ real numbers x, $f(-x) = f(x)$
(c) The graph of f is symmetric with respect to the x-axis
(d) The graph of f is symmetric with respect to the y-axis.

14. Which of the following is equivalent to the inequality $\left(\frac{1}{2}\right)^{x+2} < \left(\frac{1}{4}\right)^{7x}$?　　**14.** _____

(a) $x + 2 > 7x$　　　　　　(b) $x + 2 < 7x$
(c) $x + 2 > 14x$　　　　　(d) $x + 2 < 14x$

15. The synthetic division shown at the right
illustrates the division of $2x^3 - 3x^2 - 10x + 5$
by $d(x)$ with remainder r, where ___?___.

$$\begin{array}{r|rrrr} 3 & 2 & -3 & -10 & 5 \\ & & 6 & 9 & -3 \\ \hline & 2 & 3 & -1 & 2 \end{array}$$
15. _____

(a) $d(x) = x + 3$ and $r = 2$
(b) $d(x) = x - 3$ and $r = 2$
(c) $d(x) = x + 3$ and $r = -2$
(d) $d(x) = x - 3$ and $r = -2$

Comprehensive Test, Chapters 1–6 (page 3)

16. Which row(s) of the truth table will have the value F for $\sim(p\text{ or }q)$?

(a) I   (b) II

(c) IV   (d) I, II, and III

	p	q	$\sim(p\text{ or }q)$
I.	T	T	
II.	T	F	
III.	F	T	
IV.	F	F	

16. _____

17. Find the exact value of $\cot \frac{5\pi}{3}$.

(a) $\sqrt{3}$ (b) $-\sqrt{3}$ (c) $\frac{\sqrt{3}}{3}$ (d) $-\frac{\sqrt{3}}{3}$

17. _____

18. Which interval contains a solution of $2^x = 3x^2$?

(a) $-4 < x < -3$ (b) $-1 < x < 0$

(c) $2 < x < 3$ (d) $3 < x < 4$

18. _____

19. If f is an increasing function, which of the following is a decreasing function?

(a) $g(x) = f(x) + 5$ (b) $g(x) = e^{f(x)}$

(c) $g(x) = f(x) - 6$ (d) $g(x) = \frac{1}{f(x)}$

19. _____

20. For all α and β, $\sin(\alpha + \beta) = $ ___?___.

(a) $\sin \alpha + \sin \beta$

(b) $2 \sin \alpha \cos \beta$

(c) $\sin \alpha \cos \beta + \cos \alpha \sin \beta$

(d) $\cos \alpha \cos \beta - \sin \alpha \sin \beta$

20. _____

21. Consider the function f and $g(x) = 3 \cdot f(x)$. In which ways might f and g differ?

(a) maximum values

(b) zeros

(c) vertical asymptotes

(d) intervals where the function is increasing

21. _____

22. If r and s are odd integers and t is an even integer, which of the following is odd?

(a) $r + s + t$ (b) $3s + 1$ (c) $2(t + 7)$ (d) $(rs)^2$

22. _____

23. A function f is graphed at the right. Which statement below seems to describe f?

(a) $\lim\limits_{x \to -\infty} f(x) = 3$

(b) $\lim\limits_{x \to \infty} f(x) = 3$

(c) $\lim\limits_{x \to 3^+} f(x) = \infty$

(d) $\lim\limits_{x \to 3^+} f(x) = -\infty$

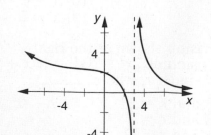

23. _____

Comprehensive Test, Chapters 1–6 (page 4)

24. If $\sin x = -\frac{1}{3}$ and $\frac{3\pi}{2} < x < 2\pi$, then $\cos x =$ ___?___.

24. _____

(a) $\frac{2}{3}$ (b) $-\frac{2}{3}$ (c) $\frac{2\sqrt{2}}{3}$ (d) $-\frac{2\sqrt{2}}{3}$

25. Which of the following is *not* true about the function $g(x) = \frac{x^2 - 6x}{x^2 - 8x + 12}$?

25. _____

(a) 2 is not in the domain of g.
(b) g has an essential discontinuity at 2.
(c) g has a removable discontinuity at 2.
(d) g has a vertical asymptote at 2.

Quiz for Lessons 7-1 Through 7-3

1. Consider the sequence defined by

$$\begin{cases} a_1 & = 1 \\ a_2 & = 3 \\ a_{k+1} & = a_k + 2a_{k-1} + 2 \ \forall \text{ integers } k \geq 2. \end{cases}$$

a. Write the first five terms of the sequence. 1. a. _____

b. Conjecture an explicit formula for a_n. b. _____

2. a. Evaluate $\displaystyle\sum_{i=1}^{8} i^3$. 2. a. _____

b. Evaluate $\dfrac{n^2(n+1)^2}{4}$ for $n = 8$ to verify the formula b. _____
$1^3 + 2^3 + 3^3 + \cdots + n^3 = \dfrac{n^2(n+1)^2}{4}$ for $n = 8$.

3. a. Write the formula that the following computer program 3. a. _____
uses to generate a sequence.

```
10   FOR J = 1 TO 25
20     TERM = 8 + (J − 1) * 5
30     PRINT TERM
40   NEXT J
50   END
```

b. Is the program using a recursive or explicit formula? b. _____

4. Rewrite $\displaystyle\sum_{i=3}^{k+1} (i^2 + 2)$ in terms of $\displaystyle\sum_{i=3}^{k} (i^2 + 2)$. 4. _____

5. Prove that the sequence defined by the recursive formula 5. _____
$$\begin{cases} b_1 & = 2 \\ b_{k+1} & = 3b_k - 2 \ \forall \text{ integers } k \geq 1 \end{cases}$$
has explicit formula $a_n = 3^{n-1} + 1$.

  Precalculus and Discrete Mathematics © Scott, Foresman and Company

Quiz for Lessons 7-1 Through 7-3   (page 2)

6. Consider the problem of determining
how many chords can be drawn
connecting a given number of points
on a circle.

a. Suppose n points have been located on the circle and
the chords determined by every combination of 2
points have been drawn. If the $(n + 1)$st point is now
added, how many additional chords can be drawn?

6. a. _____

b. Write a recurrence relation for $c_{k + 1}$, the number of
chords determined by $k + 1$ points, as well as the
initial condition for c_1.

b. _____

c. Draw diagrams to show that your recursive formula
holds for $n = 1, 2,$ and 3.

c.

Quiz for Lessons 7-4 Through 7-6

1. Consider the computer program below.

```
10   SUM = 0
20   FOR J = 1 TO 20
30      SUM = SUM + 4 * .75 ∧ J
40   NEXT J
50   PRINT SUM
```

    a. Use summation notation to write the expression the program evaluates.

    b. Find the value printed in line 50.

1. a. _____

   b. _____

2. Explain the Principle of Mathematical Induction in your own words.

2. _____

  _____

  _____

3. Suppose the following statement is to be proved by mathematical induction.

    ∀ positive integers n, 8 is a factor of $3^{2n} - 1$.

    a. What is the basis step?

3. a. _____

    b. What is the inductive assumption?

   b. _____

  _____

    c. To complete a proof by induction, what must be shown using the inductive assumption?

   c. _____

  _____

4. Use mathematical induction to prove
$$\frac{1}{2} + \frac{1}{2^2} + \frac{1}{2^3} + \cdots + \frac{1}{2^n} = 1 - \frac{1}{2^n}$$
∀ positive integers *n*.

4. _____

Chapter 7 Test, Form A

1. Write the first five terms of the sequence
$$\begin{cases} a_1 &= 3 \\ a_{k+1} &= 2a_k - 1 \end{cases} \forall \text{ integers } k \geq 1.$$

1. _____

2. Conjecture an explicit formula for the sequence given in Question 1.

2. _____

3. Someone with chickenpox infected 4 other people. Each newly infected person infected 4 more people, each of whom then infected 4 more people, and so on. Let C_n be the number of people who become infected on the nth time. Write a recursive definition for the sequence C.

3. _____

4. *True* or *false*? $\displaystyle\sum_{k=0}^{n} (n + 11)^k = \sum_{i=3}^{n} (n + 11)^{i-3}$

4. _____

5. Write the following sum using summation notation.
$$2 + 2 \cdot 3 + 3 \cdot 4 + 4 \cdot 5 + 5 \cdot 6 + 6 \cdot 7$$

5. _____

6. Write $\displaystyle\sum_{j=2}^{k+1} j(j + 2)$ in terms of $\displaystyle\sum_{j=2}^{k} j(j + 2)$.

6. _____

7. **a.** Find the value of $\displaystyle\sum_{k=0}^{4} \left(\frac{2}{5^k}\right)$.

7. **a.** _____

   b. Does $\displaystyle\sum_{k=0}^{\omega} \left(\frac{2}{5^k}\right)$ converge? If so, find its value. If not, explain why not.

   b. _____

8. What is the difference in the inductive step between the Principle of Mathematical Induction and the Strong Form of Mathematical Induction?

8. _____

_____

_____

9. Prove that the sequence defined by the recursive formula
$$\begin{cases} a_1 &= 2 \\ a_{k+1} &= 3a_k + 2 \end{cases} \forall \text{ integers } k \geq 1$$
has explicit formula $b_n = 3^n - 1$.

9. _____

Continued

Chapter 7 Test, Form A   (page 2)

10. Use the Principle of Mathematical Induction to prove that   **10.**
3 is a factor of $n^3 + 5n$ $\forall$ positive integers n.

11. Consider the sequence defined by the recursive formula

$$\begin{cases} a_1 &= 3 \\ a_2 &= 1 \\ a_3 &= 5 \\ a_{k+1} &= a_k + a_{k-1} + a_{k-2} \ \forall \text{ integers } k \geq 3. \end{cases}$$

Suppose that induction is to be used to prove that every
term of this sequence is odd.

a. What is the basis step?   **11. a.** _____

b. What is the inductive assumption?   **b.** _____

c. What is to be proved from the inductive assumption?   **c.** _____

12. Determine the limit of the values printed by the computer   **12.** _____
program below.

```
10   K = 0
20   SUM = 0
30   SUM = SUM + (1/3) ∧ K
40   PRINT SUM
50   K = K + 1
60   GOTO 30
```

13. Use the Quicksort algorithm to sort the list 2, 5, 1, 3, 4.   **13.** _____
Show the results at each step.

_____

_____

Precalculus and Discrete Mathematics © Scott, Foresman and Company

Chapter 7 Test, Form B

1. Write the first five terms of the sequence

$$\begin{cases} a_1 = 0 \\ a_{k+1} = a_k + 2k + 1 \ \forall \text{ integers } k \geq 1. \end{cases}$$

1. _____

2. Conjecture an explicit formula for the sequence given in Question 1.

2. _____

3. A person begins spreading a rumor by telling it to 5 people, each of whom tells it to 5 other people, and so on. Let R_n be the number of people who have heard the rumor on the nth time. Write a recursive definition for the sequence R.

3. _____

4. *True* or *false*? $\displaystyle\sum_{j=1}^{m} (x+6)^j = \sum_{k=3}^{m+2} (x+6)^{k-2}$

4. _____

5. Write the following sum using summation notation.

$$0 + \frac{1}{2} + \frac{2}{3} + \frac{3}{4} + \frac{4}{5} + \frac{5}{6} + \frac{6}{7}$$

5. _____

6. Write $\displaystyle\sum_{i=0}^{n+1} (i^2 + 1)$ in terms of $\displaystyle\sum_{i=0}^{n} (i^2 + 1)$.

6. _____

7. a. Find the value of $\displaystyle\sum_{k=0}^{4} \left(\frac{3}{4^k}\right)$.

7. a. _____

b. Does $\displaystyle\sum_{k=0}^{\infty} \left(\frac{3}{4^k}\right)$ converge? If so, find its value. If not, explain why not.

b. _____

8. What is the difference in the basis step between the Strong Form of Mathematical Induction and the Principle of Mathematical Induction?

8. _____

_____

_____

9. Prove that the sequence defined by the recursive formula

$$\begin{cases} a_1 = 2 \\ a_{k+1} = 2a_k + 1 \ \forall \text{ integers } k \geq 1 \end{cases}$$

has explicit formula $b_n = 3 \cdot 2^{n-1} - 1$.

9. _____

Chapter 7 Test, Form B   (page 2)

10. Use the Principle of Mathematical Induction to prove that   **10.**
6 is a factor of $2n^3 + 4n$ $\forall$ positive integers n.

11. Consider the sequence defined by the recursive formula

$$\begin{cases} a_1 & = 1 \\ a_2 & = 5 \\ a_3 & = 3 \\ a_{k+1} & = 2a_k + a_{k-1} + 4a_{k-2} \ \forall \text{ integers } k \geq 3. \end{cases}$$

Suppose that induction is to be used to prove that every
term of this sequence is odd.

a. What is the basis step?   **11. a.** _____

b. What is the inductive assumption?   **b.** _____

c. What is to be proved from the inductive assumption?   **c.** _____

12. Determine the limit of the values printed by the computer   **12.** _____
program below.

```
10   J = 0
20   SUM = 0
30   SUM = SUM + (2/3) ^ J
40   PRINT SUM
50   J = J + 1
60   GOTO 30
```

13. Use the Bubblesort algorithm to sort the list 5, 9, 2, 6, 8.   **13.** _____
Show the results at each step.

_____

_____

Precalculus and Discrete Mathematics © Scott, Foresman and Company

Chapter 7 Test, Cumulative Form

You will need an automatic grapher for this test.

1. A sheet of paper is repeatedly folded in half. Let r_n be the number of regions separated by the creases in the paper after n folds. Write a recursive formula for the sequence r.

1. _____

   _____

2. In a particular car, the right side-view mirror is in line with the dashboard, 42 inches to the right of the driver. Write a formula for θ, the angle the driver must turn his head to look at the mirror, in terms of d, the distance between the driver and the dashboard.

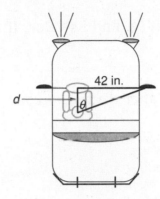

2. _____

3. Write the following sum using summation notation.
   $$3^4 + 4^5 + 5^6 + 6^7 + 7^8 + 8^9 + 9^{10}$$

3. _____

4. Solve $\tan x > -1$ for $0 \le x < 2\pi$.

4. _____

5. Give the exact value (in radians) of $\cos^{-1}\left(-\frac{\sqrt{2}}{2}\right)$.

5. _____

6. Give an example of two irrational numbers whose product is irrational.

6. _____

7. Consider the sequence defined by
   $$\begin{cases} a_1 = 2 \\ a_{k+1} = a_k + 2k + 1 \ \forall \text{ integers } k \ge 1. \end{cases}$$

   a. Write the first five terms of the sequence.

   7. a. _____

   b. Conjecture an explicit formula for a_n.
      (Hint: Each term is one more than what number?)

   b. _____

   c. Prove that your conjecture is correct.

   c.

Continued **73**

Chapter 7 Test, Cumulative Form   (page 2)

8. Give the smallest positive integer x for which
$x \equiv -83 \pmod{19}$.

8.  _____

9. a. Find the value of $\displaystyle\sum_{i=1}^{5} \frac{7}{10^i}$.

9. a. _____

b. Does $\displaystyle\sum_{i=1}^{\infty} \frac{7}{10^i}$ converge? If so, find its value. If not,
explain why not.

b. _____

10. Write the list 5, 3, 1, 9, 2 after the first, second, and third
passes of Bubblesort.

10. _____

_____

_____

11. a. Graph $f(x) = \dfrac{3x - 1}{x - 2}$.

11. a.

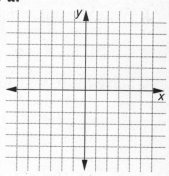

b. Use limit notation to describe the end behavior of f.

b. _____

c. Write the equation(s) of any vertical asymptote(s).

c. _____

12. Prove the following identity and give its domain.
$(\sin x + \cos x)^2 = 1 + \sin 2x$

12. _____

Chapter 7 Test, Cumulative Form   (page 3)

13. Let c be the sequence defined by the recursive formula

$$\begin{cases} c_1 & = 10 \\ c_2 & = 5 \\ c_{k+1} & = c_k + 2c_{k-1} \ \forall \text{ integers } k \geq 2. \end{cases}$$

Suppose induction is to be used to prove that every term of the sequence is a multiple of 5.

a. What is the basis step?

13. a. _____

b. What is the inductive assumption?

b. _____

c. What is to be proved from the inductive assumption?

c. _____

14. Use mathematical induction to prove that the following statement is true for all integers $n \geq 1$.

14.

$$\sum_{i=1}^{n} \frac{1}{(2i-1)(2i+1)} = \frac{n}{2n+1}$$

Quiz for Lessons 8-1 Through 8-3

In 1 and 2, a complex number is given in one of four possible forms. Write it in the other three forms.

1. (5, 12)

1. _____

_____

_____

2. $4\left(\cos \frac{3\pi}{4} + i \sin \frac{3\pi}{4}\right)$

2. _____

_____

_____

In 3 and 4, find zw and $\frac{z}{w}$. Express your answers in the same form as z and w.

3. $z = 2(\cos 150° + i \sin 150°)$
   $w = 2(\cos 315° + i \sin 315°)$

3. _____

_____

4. $z = (-2, -1)$
   $w = (5, -2)$

4. _____

_____

5. Illustrate the multiplication of z by w in Question 4 with a diagram that verifies the Geometric Multiplication Theorem.

5.

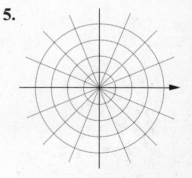

6. Use Ohm's Law to find the current in an electrical circuit with impedance $3 + 2i$ ohms and voltage 10.

6. _____

7. Prove that if z is a complex number, then $\frac{1}{z} = \frac{\bar{z}}{|z|^2}$.

7.

Precalculus and Discrete Mathematics © Scott, Foresman and Company

Quiz for Lessons 8-4 Through 8-7

In 1 and 2, sketch graphs of the polar equations and write the name of each curve.

1. $r = 1 + 3 \cos \theta$

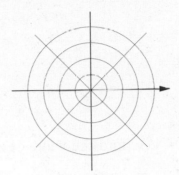

1. _____

2. $r = \dfrac{\theta}{2\pi} + 1$

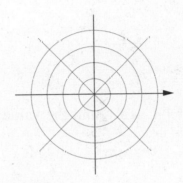

2. _____

3. Calculate z^7 when $z = 2(\cos 20° + i \sin 20°)$.

3. _____

4. Find and graph the sixth roots of $32 + 32\sqrt{3}i$.

4. _____

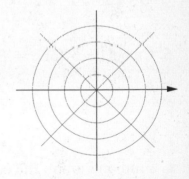

5. For a real number w and a positive integer n, how many real nth roots does w have if:

   a. w is positive and n is odd?

   b. w is positive and n is even?

   c. w is negative and n is odd?

   d. w is negative and n is even?

5. a. _____

   b. _____

   c. _____

   d. _____

6. Let n and m be positive integers and $z = [r, \theta]$. Show that $\dfrac{z^n}{z^m} = z^{n-m}$. (Hint: Use DeMoivre's Theorem.)

Chapter 8 Test, Form A

1. Write each complex number in $a + bi$ form and polar form.

   a. (-3, 4)

                                                       1. a. _____

   b. $3(\cos \pi + i \sin \pi)$ b. _____

2. If $z = 2 + 2\sqrt{3}i$ and $w = \sqrt{3}i$, find the value of each expression.

   a. $z - \overline{w}$ 2. a. _____

   b. $\frac{z}{w}$ b. _____

3. If $z = [3, 120°]$ and $w = [-1, -15°]$, find the value of $\overline{z}w$.   3. _____

4. Use Ohm's Law to find the voltage in an AC circuit with current $\frac{100}{29} + \frac{40}{29}i$ amps and impedance $5 - 2i$ ohms.   4. _____

5. Calculate z^5 for $z = [2\sqrt{5}, 72°]$.   5. _____

6. Find and graph the cube roots of -216.   6. _____

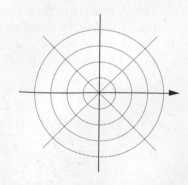

                                               Precalculus and Discrete Mathematics © Scott, Foresman and Company

Chapter 8 Test, Form A   (page 2)

In 7 and 8, graph the polar equation and identify the curve obtained.

7. $r = 2 \cos 6\theta$

7. _____

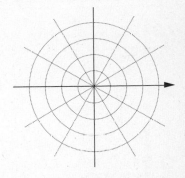

8. $r = 5 - 3 \sin \theta$

8. _____

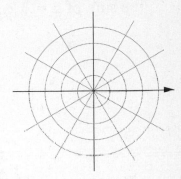

9. Find all zeros and the corresponding multiplicities for the polynomial $p(x) = x^4 - 4x^3 + 8x^2 - 16x + 16$, given that $2i$ is a zero of $p(x)$.

9. _____

10. The graph of a fifth degree polynomial function p is given at the right. Sketch the x-axis so that p has three real zeros, two of which have multiplicity two.

10.

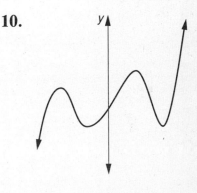

11. According to the Fundamental Theorem of Algebra, $p(x) = 5x^5 - 3x^2 + 2xi - 8$ has exactly ___?___ complex zeros counting multiplicities.

11. _____

Continued **79**

Chapter 8 Test, Form A   (page 3)

12. Prove that if z is any complex number, then $z - \bar{z}$ is an imaginary number.

12.

13. Verify the Geometric Addition Theorem by illustrating the sum of $z = 3 + 2i$ and $w = -1 + 2i$ at the right.

13.

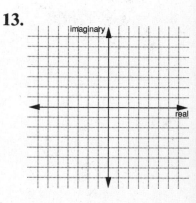

14. Give one pair of polar coordinates for the point with rectangular coordinates (-4, -4).

14.  _____

Precalculus and Discrete Mathematics © Scott, Foresman and Company

Chapter 8 Test, Form B

1. Write each complex number in $a + bi$ form and in polar form.

   a. $(0, -4)$

1. a. _____

_____

   b. $3\left(\cos \frac{\pi}{3} + i \sin \frac{\pi}{3}\right)$

b. _____

_____

2. If $z = 3 + 4\sqrt{3}i$ and $w = 2 - \sqrt{3}i$, find the value of each expression.

   a. zw

2. a. _____

   b. $z + \overline{w}$

b. _____

3. If $z = [2, -45°]$ and $w = [5, -150°]$, find the value of $\frac{z}{w}$.

3. _____

4. Use Ohm's Law to find the current in an AC circuit with impedance $4 + 4\sqrt{3}i$ ohms and voltage 15 volts.

4. _____

5. Calculate z^9 for $z = \left[2, \frac{\pi}{4}\right]$. Express your answer in trigonometric form.

5. _____

6. Find and graph the fifth roots of $1 + i$.

6. _____

Chapter 8 Test, Form B (page 2)

In 7 and 8, graph the polar equation and identify the curve obtained.

7. $r = 1 + 3 \sin \theta$

7. _____

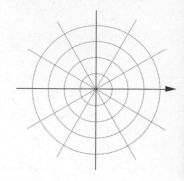

8. $r = 1 + 2\theta$

8. _____

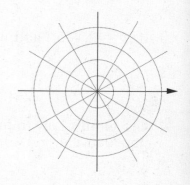

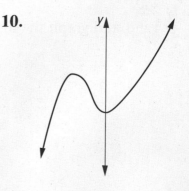

9. Find all zeros and the corresponding multiplicities for the polynomial $p(x) = 8x^4 + 4x^3 + 6x^2 + 9x - 27$, given that $\frac{3}{2}i$ is a zero of $p(x)$.

9. _____

10. The graph of a third degree polynomial function p is given at the right. Sketch the x-axis so that p has two real zeros, one of multiplicity two.

10.

11. According to the Fundamental Theorem of Algebra, $f(x) = 4x^7 + 3x^2 - 2$ has exactly __?__ complex zeros, counting multiplicities.

11. _____

Precalculus and Discrete Mathematics © Scott, Foresman and Company

12. Prove that the product of any complex number and its complex conjugate is a real number.

12.

13. Illustrate the Geometric Multiplication Theorem for $z = \left[2, \frac{\pi}{6}\right]$ and $w = \left[3, \frac{\pi}{3}\right]$ at the right.

13.

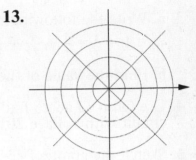

14. Give one pair of polar coordinates for the point with rectangular coordinates (5, -5).

14. _____

Chapter 8 Test, Cumulative Form

1. Find the sum of the complex numbers (3, 2) and $\left[2\sqrt{2}, \frac{\pi}{4}\right]$. Express the result in binomial form.

1. _____

2. Graph the complex numbers and their sum from Question 1 to verify the Geometric Addition Theorem.

2.

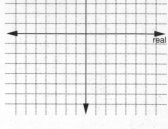

3. a. Write the following series using summation notation.
$$1 + \frac{1}{3} + \frac{1}{9} + \frac{1}{27} + \frac{1}{81} + \cdots$$

3. a. _____

b. Find the value of the series.

b. _____

4. Use Ohm's Law to find the current in an AC electrical circuit with voltage 20 volts and impedance $6 + 8i$ ohms.

4. _____

5. Sketch the graph of $r = 3 \cos \theta$ and write the name of the curve.

5. _____

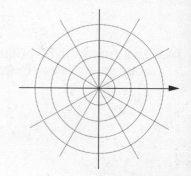

6. Find and graph the complex solutions to the equation $z^5 = \left[32, \frac{5\pi}{8}\right]$.

6. _____

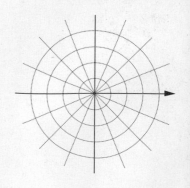

Precalculus and Discrete Mathematics © Scott, Foresman and Company

Chapter 8 Test, Cumulative Form   (page 2)

7. Calculate z^n if $z = \left[1.1, \frac{2\pi}{3} \right]$ and $n = 14$.

8. Give a polynomial of degree 4 with all real coefficients that has zeros 2, -3, and -2i.

9. Use the Principle of Mathematical Induction to prove that $n^3 + 2n$ is divisible by 3 ∀ positive integers.

9.

10. Find the first five terms of the sequence defined by

$$\begin{cases} a_1 = 3 \\ a_2 = 2 \\ a_k = 2a_{k-1} + ka_{k-2} + 4 \ \forall\ k \geq 3. \end{cases}$$

10. _____

11. Apply the Quicksort algorithm to the list

   5, 1, 10, 12, 3, 2, 11.

   Draw a diagram to show your work.

11. _____

Chapter 8 Test, Cumulative Form   (page 3)

12. Consider the function f defined by $f(x) = \dfrac{x^2 + 6x + 8}{x^2 + 5x + 6}$.

    a. Use limit notation to describe the end behavior of f.   **12. a.** _____

    b. Classify any discontinuities as removable or essential.   **b.** _____

    c. Find the equations of all asymptotes to the graph of f.   **c.** _____

13. Write the standard prime factorization of 3,861.   **13.** _____

14. a. Perform the addition 11010_2 **14. a.** _____
                     $+\ 11001_2$

    b. Convert your answer to base 10.   **b.** _____

Precalculus and Discrete Mathematics © Scott, Foresman and Company

Quiz for Lessons 9-1 Through 9-3

1. The table below gives the number of lawyers in the U.S. between 1960 and 1985, as reported in the *Statistical Abstract of the United States 1988*.

Year	Number of Lawyers
1960	285,933
1963	296,069
1966	316,656
1970	355,242
1980	542,205
1985	655,191

   a. Find the average rate of change in the number of lawyers from 1960 to 1980.

1. a. _____

   b. Find the average rate of change in the number of lawyers from 1980 to 1985.

    b. _____

   c. Compare your answers to parts a and b and explain what this means in terms of the number of lawyers in the U.S.

    c. _____

_____

_____

2. Write the definition of the derivative of a function f at x.

2. _____

3. Use the definition of derivative to find the derivative of f when $f(x) = 7x - 1$.

3. _____

4. Consider the function g graphed at the right.

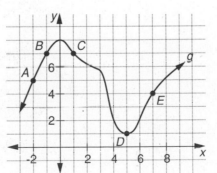

   a. In going from A to B, what is Δy?

4. a. _____

   b. What is the average rate of change in going from C to D?

    b. _____

   c. Sketch the tangent line at E on the graph above.

   d. Is $g'(4)$ positive, negative, or zero?

    d. _____

Quiz for Lessons 9-1 Through 9-3　(page 2)

5. The height (in feet) after t seconds of a batted ball with initial vertical velocity 70 ft/sec is given by $h(t) = 70t - 16t^2$.

   a. Find a formula for the average vertical velocity of the ball from time t to time $t + \Delta t$.

   b. Use the formula in part **a** to find the average vertical velocity from time 4 seconds to time 5 seconds.

   c. Find the derivative of h.

   d. What is the ball's instantaneous vertical velocity at time 4 seconds?

5. a. _____

   b. _____

   c. _____

   d. _____

 Precalculus and Discrete Mathematics © Scott, Foresman and Company

Chapter 9 Test, Form A

1. The table at the right shows the money spent by NASA on research and development for certain years from 1975 to 1985.

Year	Amount Spent (in millions of dollars)
1975	3,064
1980	3,234
1981	3,593
1982	3,078
1983	2,662
1984	2,822
1985	3,327

a. Find the average rate of change from 1983 to 1984.

1. a. _____

b. Find the average rate of change from 1975 to 1980.

b. _____

c. Interpret the answers to parts a and b in terms of NASA spending.

c. _____

_____

2. Refer to the graph of the function g below.

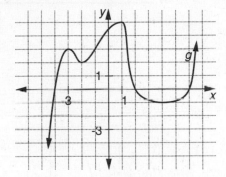

a. Find the average rate of change from $x = -1$ to $x = 2$.

2. a. _____

b. *Multiple choice.* Over which of the following intervals is the average rate of change zero?

(a) $x = -4$ to $x = 4$ (b) $x = -3$ to $x = -1$
(c) $x = -3$ to $x = 1$ (d) $x = -2$ to $x = 2$

b. _____

c. *Multiple choice.* Over which interval is the average rate of change 1?

(a) $x = -3$ to $x = -2$ (b) $x = -2$ to $x = -1$
(c) $x = 1$ to $x = 2$ (d) $x = -4$ to $x = 0$

c. _____

d. What is the average rate of change from $x = 1$ to $x = 2$?

d. _____

3. Let $h(x) = 5x^2 + 1$.

    a. Find a formula for the average rate of change of the function h from 3 to $3 + \Delta x$.

    b. Use the answer to part **a** to find the average rate of change from 3 to 3.25.

3. a. _____

    b. _____

4. *Multiple choice.* Let f be a function defined by $f(x) = x^3$. Which of the following equals $f'(x)$?

    (a) $(x + \Delta x)^3 - x^3$

    (b) $\dfrac{(x + \Delta x)^3 - x^3}{\Delta x}$

    (c) $\lim\limits_{\Delta x \to 0} \dfrac{(x + \Delta x)^3}{\Delta x}$

    (d) $\lim\limits_{x \to 0} \dfrac{(x + \Delta x)^3 - x^3}{\Delta x}$

    (e) $\lim\limits_{\Delta x \to 0} \dfrac{(x + \Delta x)^3 - x^3}{\Delta x}$

4. _____

5. Refer to the graph in Exercise 2. Estimate $g'(-2.5)$.

5. _____

6. *Multiple choice.* The graph at the right is the graph of $f'(x)$. Which of the graphs below could be the graph of f?

6. _____

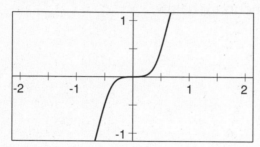

(a)
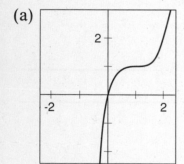

(b)
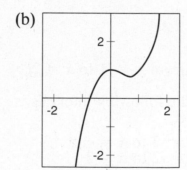

(c)
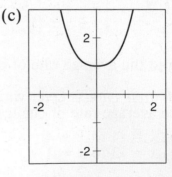

7. For the function g graphed at the right, is the second derivative positive or negative on the interval $0 < x < 3$?

7. _____

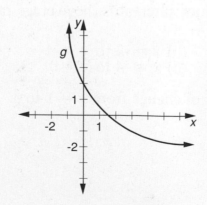

Precalculus and Discrete Mathematics © Scott, Foresman and Company

Chapter 9 Test, Form A (page 3)

8. A ball is thrown so that its height (in feet) after t seconds is given by $h(t) = -16t^2 + 48t + 40$.

a. Find the instantaneous velocity of the ball 2 seconds after it is thrown.

8. a. _____

b. Find the acceleration of the ball 2 seconds after it is thrown.

b. _____

9. a. Find the maximum height reached by the ball in Exercise 8.

9. a. _____

b. Find the instantaneous velocity when the ball reaches its maximum height.

b. _____

10. If $h(x) = \ln x^2$, then $h'(x) = \frac{2}{x}$.

a. Identify the interval(s) on which h is increasing.

10. a. _____

b. Identify the interval(s) on which h is decreasing.

b. _____

11. a. If $g(x) = -7x^2 + 5$, use the definition of derivative to find a formula for $g'(x)$.

11. a. _____

b. Explain how your answer to part **a** agrees with the theorem for the derivative of a quadratic function.

b. _____

_____

Chapter 9 Test, Form B

1. The table at the right gives the number of undergraduate students enrolled in the School of Science at Purdue University each year from 1973 to 1983.

   Source: *Purdue University*

Year	Number of Students
1973	2,689
1974	2,628
1975	2,727
1976	2,586
1977	2,565
1978	2,538
1979	2,453
1980	2,463
1981	2,766
1982	2,809
1983	2,921

a. Find the average rate of change from 1973 to 1980.

1. a. _____

b. Find the average rate of change from 1981 to 1983.

b. _____

c. Interpret the answers to parts **a** and **b** in terms of numbers of students enrolled.

c. _____

_____

2. Refer to the graph of function *f* below.

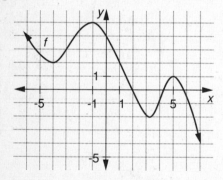

a. Find the average rate of change from $x = -3$ to $x = 2$.

2. a. _____

b. *Multiple choice.* Over which of the following intervals is the average rate of change zero?

b. _____

(a) $x = -6$ to $x = -1$ (b) $x = 1$ to $x = 5$
(c) $x = -4$ to $x = -1$ (d) $x = -4$ to $x = 1$

c. *Multiple choice.* Over which interval is the average rate of change 1?

c. _____

(a) $x = -6$ to $x = -3$ (b) $x = -6$ to $x = 0$
(c) $x = -6$ to $x = 6$ (d) $x = -4$ to $x = -1$

d. What is the average rate of change from $x = -1$ to $x = 1$?

d. _____

Precalculus and Discrete Mathematics © Scott, Foresman and Company

Chapter 9 Test, Form B (page 2)

3. Let $k(x) = 3x^2 - 5$.

   a. Find a formula for the average rate of change of the function k from 2 to $2 + \Delta x$.

   3. a. _____

   b. Use the answer to part **a** to find the average rate of change from 2 to 2.5.

   b. _____

4. *Multiple choice.* Let g be a function defined by $g(x) = 7x^2$. Which of the following equals $g'(x)$?

   4. _____

   (a) $7(x + \Delta x)^2 - 7x^2$

   (b) $\lim\limits_{\Delta x \to 0} \dfrac{7(x + \Delta x)^2}{\Delta x}$

   (c) $\lim\limits_{x \to 0} \dfrac{7(x + \Delta x)^2 - 7x^2}{\Delta x}$

   (d) $\lim\limits_{\Delta x \to 0} \dfrac{7(x + \Delta x)^2 - 7x^2}{\Delta x}$

   (e) $\dfrac{7(x + \Delta x)^2 - 7x^2}{\Delta x}$

5. Refer to the graph in Exercise 2. Estimate $f'(.5)$.

   5. _____

6. *Multiple choice.*
The graph at the right is the graph of $f'(x)$. Which of the graphs below could be the graph of f?

   6. _____

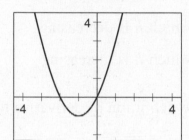

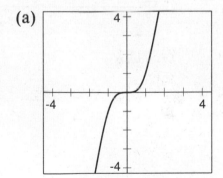

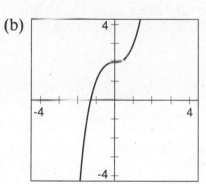

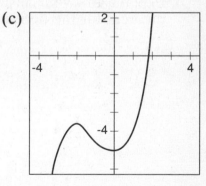

(a)   (b)   (c)

7. For the function h graphed at the right, is the second derivative positive or negative on the interval $0 < x < 5$?

   7. _____

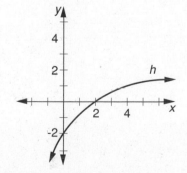

Chapter 9 Test, Form B   (page 3)

8. A ball is thrown so that its height (in meters) after t seconds is given by $h(t) = -4.9t^2 + 49t + 21$.

   a. Find the instantaneous velocity of the ball 3 seconds after it is thrown.

   8. a. _____

   b. Find the acceleration of the ball 3 seconds after it is thrown.

   b. _____

9. a. Find the maximum height reached by the ball in Exercise 8.

   9. a. _____

   b. Find the instantaneous velocity when the ball reaches its maximum height.

   b. _____

10. If $h(x) = \ln (x - 5)^2$, then $h'(x) = \dfrac{2}{x - 5}$.

   a. Identify the interval(s) on which h is decreasing.

   10. a. _____

   b. Identify the interval(s) on which h is increasing.

   b. _____

11. a. If $f(x) = -6x^2 + 10$, use the definition of derivative to find a formula for $g'(x)$.

   11. a. _____

   b. Explain how your answer to part **a** agrees with the theorem for the derivative of a quadratic function.

   b. _____

Chapter 9 Test, Cumulative Form

1. *Multiple choice.* The graph at the right is the graph of *f*. Which of the graphs below could be the graph of *f'*?

1. _____

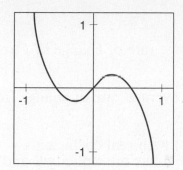

(a)

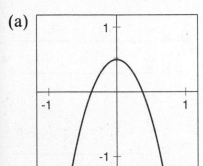

(b)

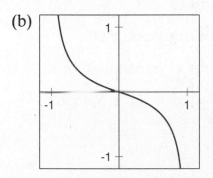

(c)

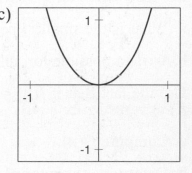

2. Find the rectangular coordinates for the point *P* whose polar coordinates are given.

2. a. _____

a. $\left[4, -\frac{2\pi}{3}\right]$ **b.** [5, 135°]

b. _____

3. Refer to the graph of the function *g* at the right.

3. a. _____

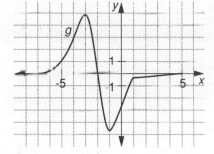

a. Find the average rate of change from *x* = -5 to *x* = -2.

b. *Multiple choice.* Over which of the following intervals is the average rate of change positive?

b. _____

(a) *x* = -3 to *x* = 1   (b) *x* = -5 to *x* = -2
(c) *x* = -1 to *x* = 5   (d) *x* = -5 to *x* = 5

c. Estimate the derivative of *g* at *x* = -1.

c. _____

d. Identify the interval(s) over which *g'*(*x*) > 0.

d. _____

4. Let $h(x) = \frac{2x - 6}{x^2 - 9}$.

a. Is the discontinuity at *x* = 3 essential or removable?

4. a. _____

b. Describe the end behavior of *h*.

b. _____

c. Find $\lim_{x \to 3^+} h(x)$.

c. _____

Chapter 9 Test, Cumulative Form   (page 2)

5. Let $f(x) = x^2 + 6x - 5$.

   a. Find a formula for the average rate of change of f from x to $x + \Delta x$.

      5. a. _____

   b. Use the formula to find the average rate of change from -5 to -1.

      b. _____

6. The zeros of a polynomial $p(x)$ with real coefficients include $2 + i$, $-i$, 3, and 0. The 0 has multiplicity 2 and the other zeros have multiplicity 1.

   a. What is the smallest possible degree of $p(x)$?

      6. a. _____

   b. Write a possible formula for $p(x)$ in factored form.

      b. _____

7. Use the fact that if $f(x) = 2x^3 - x^2 - 4x + 5$, then $f'(x) = 6x^2 - 2x - 4$.

   a. Compute $f''(x)$.

      7. a. _____

   b. Determine the intervals on which f is increasing.

      b. _____

   c. Use f' to find possible relative minima and maxima.

      c. _____

8. a. $-1 + \sqrt{3}i$ is a cube root of what real number?

      8. a. _____

   b. What are the other cube roots?

      b. _____

   c. Graph these cube roots on the polar grid at the right.

      c.

9. A projectile is propelled upward with an initial velocity of 250 ft/sec. Its height (in feet) after t seconds is given by $h(t) = 250t - 16t^2$.

   a. Find the velocity function.

      9. a. _____

   b. What is the projectile's velocity after 6 seconds?

      b. _____

   c. Find its acceleration after 6 seconds.

      c. _____

   d. What is the maximum height it reaches?

      d. _____

10. Solve the equation $\log(x - 21) + \log x = 2$.

      10. _____

Precalculus and Discrete Mathematics © Scott, Foresman and Company

Comprehensive Test, Chapters 1-9

In 1–25, write the letter of the correct answer on the line. You will need an automatic grapher for this test.

1. If $\sin x = \frac{1}{4}$ and $\cos x = \frac{\sqrt{15}}{4}$, then $\cot x = \underline{\quad ? \quad}$.

   (a) $\sqrt{15}$ (b) $\frac{4}{\sqrt{15}}$ (c) $\frac{\sqrt{15}}{15}$ (d) 4

1. _____

2. Find the statement which is logically equivalent to
    If figure ABCD is a square, then it has four equal sides.

   (a) If figure $ABCD$ has four equal sides, then it is a square.
   (b) If figure $ABCD$ does not have four equal sides, then it is a square.
   (c) If figure $ABCD$ is not a square, then it does not have four equal sides.
   (d) If figure $ABCD$ does not have four equal sides, then it is not a square.

2. _____

3. Which of the following is a factor of $x^9 + 2x^4 - 1$?

   (a) $x - 2$ (b) $x + 1$
   (c) $x - 1$ (d) $x^2 + 1$

3. _____

4. Which of the following defines a function that is continuous on the interval $-2 \le x \le 4$?

   (a) $f(x) = \frac{3}{x}$ (b) $g(x) = \lfloor x \rfloor$
   (c) $h(x) = \frac{x}{x + 3}$ (d) $p(x) = \sqrt{x + 1}$

4. _____

5. Find all possible values of r such that $\sum\limits_{k=0}^{\infty} ar^k$ converges.

   (a) $r \ge 0$ (b) $0 \le r \le 1$
   (c) $|r| < 1$ (d) $r > -1$

5. _____

6. Which of the following is equal to $\cos^2 x - \sin^2 x$ for all x?

   (a) 1   (b) $\cos \frac{1}{2}x$ (c) $\cos 2x$ (d) $\sin 2x$

6. _____

7. If $A_n = \frac{2n}{n + 1}$, find $\lim\limits_{n \to \infty} A_n$.

   (a) 2   (b) 1   (c) ∞ (d) 0

7. _____

8 Which of the following is an equation of a circle in polar coordinates?

   (a) $r = 2 \sin \theta$ (b) $r = 2 \cos \theta$
   (c) $r = \theta$ (d) $r = 1 - 2 \sin \theta$

8. _____

Comprehensive Test, Chapters 1–9 (page 2)

9. Which formula gives the derivative of f when $f(x) = 6x^2 - 5x + 10$?　　**9.** _____

(a) $f'(x) = 6x - 5$ 　　　　　　　(b) $f'(x) = 2x - 5$
(c) $f'(x) = 12x^2 - 5x$ 　　　　　(d) $f'(x) = 12x - 5$

10. Which graph represents the solution set of the inequality　　**10.** _____
$|x + 2| \le 4$?

(a)
　　-4　　0　　4

(b)
　　-6　　　0　2

(c)
　　-4　　0　　4

(d)
　　-6　　　0　2

11. What is the binary representation of 63?　　**11.** _____

(a) 11111_2 　　　　　　　　　(b) 101111_2
(c) 101100_2 　　　　　　　　(d) 111111_2

12. If $f'(x) = (x + 1)(x - 2)$, find the interval on which f is decreasing.　　**12.** _____

(a) $x < -1$ 　　　　　　　　　(b) $-2 < x < 1$
(c) $-1 < x < 2$ 　　　　　　　(d) $x < 0$

13. A polynomial $p(x)$ with real coefficients has the following zeros: 2, -1,　　**13.** _____
0, and i. Which of the following is a possible formula for $p(x)$ in
factored form?

(a) $p(x) = x(x - 2)(x + 1)(x^2 + 1)$
(b) $p(x) = x(x - 2)(x + 1)(x - i)$
(c) $p(x) = x(x + 2)(x - 1)(x + i)$
(d) $p(x) = x(x + 2)(x - 1)(x^2 + 1)$

14. Which of the following functions has a vertical asymptote?　　**14.** _____

(a) $y = 2^x$ 　　　　　　　　　(b) $y = \dfrac{2}{x - 3}$
(c) $y = \sqrt{x + 1}$ 　　　　　　(d) $y = 5x^3 - 6$

15. If $\sin x = \dfrac{4}{5}$ and $0 < x < \dfrac{\pi}{2}$, then $\sin 2x = $ ___?___.　　**15.** _____

(a) $-\dfrac{24}{25}$ 　　　(b) $\dfrac{24}{25}$ 　　　(c) $\dfrac{8}{5}$ 　　　(d) $\dfrac{16}{25}$

Comprehensive Test, Chapters 1–9 (page 3)

16. Which of the following represents the infinite sum

$\frac{1}{2 \cdot 3} + \frac{2}{3 \cdot 4} + \frac{3}{4 \cdot 5} + \frac{4}{5 \cdot 6} + \cdots$?

16. _____

(a) $\displaystyle\sum_{k=0}^{\infty} \frac{k}{(k + 1)(k + 2)}$

(b) $\displaystyle\sum_{k=1}^{n} \frac{k}{(k + 1)(k + 2)}$

(c) $\displaystyle\sum_{k=1}^{\infty} \frac{1}{(k + 1)(k + 2)}$

(d) $\displaystyle\sum_{k=0}^{\infty} \frac{k + 1}{(k + 2)(k + 3)}$

17. For all positive x, y, and z, $2 \log x + \log y - \log z = $ ___?___.

17. _____

(a) $\log \left(\frac{x^2 y}{z}\right)$

(b) $\log (x^2 + y - z)$

(c) $\log \left(\frac{2xy}{z}\right)$

(d) $2 \log \left(\frac{xy}{z}\right)$

18. If a, b, and c are integers, and $a + b$ and $b + c$ are both odd, what can be concluded about $a + c$?

18. _____

(a) It is odd.

(b) It is odd if a is even.

(c) It is even.

(d) None of the above

19. What is the 1,225th term of the sequence defined by $a_n = \cos \left(\frac{n\pi}{2}\right)$?

19. _____

(a) 1

(b) -1

(c) 0

(d) $\frac{\sqrt{2}}{2}$

20. Which of the following defines the function graphed at the right?

20. _____

(a) $y = 4 \sin \frac{\theta}{2}$

(b) $y = 4 \sin 2\theta$

(c) $y = 4 \cos 2\theta$

(d) $y = 4 \cos \theta$

Comprehensive Test, Chapters 1–9 (page 4)

21. Which of the following is a 1-1 function?

21. _____

(a)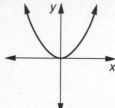

(b)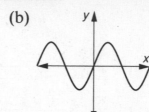

(c)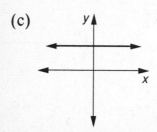

(d)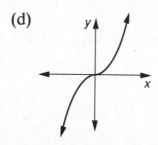

22. What is the slope of the line tangent to the function $g(x) = 2x^2 + 5x - 7$ at $x = 2$?

22. _____

(a) 11   (b) -9   (c) -7   (d) 13

23. Which of the following is *not* equal to [5, 60°]?

23. _____

(a) [-5, -60°]   (b) [5, -300°]
(c) [-5, 240°]   (d) [5, 420°]

24. If $\frac{1}{x-1} + \frac{1}{x+1} = -\frac{4}{3}$, find x.

24. _____

(a) $x = 2, -\frac{1}{2}$ (b) $x = -2, \frac{1}{2}$

(c) $x = 3$ (d) $x = -\frac{1}{3}$

25. Which of the following defines an even function?

25. _____

(a) $y = x^3 + 2$ (b) $y = \sqrt{x}$
(c) $y = \cos \theta$ (d) $y = e^x$

Precalculus and Discrete Mathematics © Scott, Foresman and Company

NAME _____

Quiz for Lessons 10-1 Through 10-3

1. Which cell of the diagram describes the problem of finding the number of 7-digit ID numbers that can be assigned to students?

1. _____

	Repetition of symbols allowed	Repetition of symbols not allowed
Ordered symbols		
Unordered symbols		

2. At a carnival, a children's game consists of picking one of three rubber ducks from a tub.

One is marked on the bottom to indicate a prize is won. If a child does not win, he draws again until he does. Draw a possibility tree to show all possible sequences of choices, assuming B is the winning duck.

2. _____

3. Explain the essential difference between the two counting problems below.

3. _____

_____

_____

A: A store carries a mix-and-match clothing line. The 5 skirts and 8 blouses all match. A woman decides to buy 2 skirts and 2 blouses. How many different ways can she make this choice?

B: The senior class elects a prom king and queen along with a runner-up for each honor. This year, 5 boys and 8 girls have been nominated. In how many ways can the decision be made?

4. Eleven books are to be displayed side-by-side on a shelf in a library. How many different arrangements are possible?

4. _____

Quiz for Lessons 10-1 Through 10-3 (page 2)

5. The diagram below shows the different methods of transportation that can be used to travel from the airport to a hotel. How many different routes are possible?

5. _____

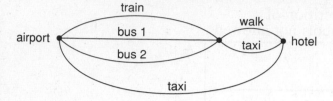

6. Evaluate $P(10, 4)$.

6. _____

7. Consider the identity $P(n, r) \cdot P(n - r, s) = P(n, r + s)$ for positive integers n, r, and s such that $r < n$ and $s < n - r$.

a. Verify the identity for $n = 9$, $r = 4$, and $s = 2$.

7 a. _____

_____

b. Prove the identity.

b.

Quiz for Lessons 10-4 Through 10-6

In 1-4, write *P* or *C* to tell whether the number can best be found using permutations or combinations.

1. the number of different ways of assigning positions to 9 members of a baseball team

1. _____

2. the number of 7-card hands that can be dealt from a 52-card deck

2. _____

3. the number of ways to choose 3 spices to flavor a sauce from a collection of 14 spices

3. _____

4. the number of ways that horses can win (come in first), place (come in second), or show (come in third) in a race

4. _____

5. Evaluate $C(100, 5)$.

5. _____

6. At a chicken farm, eggs are put into boxes of one dozen. If the probability that any particular egg is rotten is 1%, what is the probability that a box will have no more than one rotten egg?

6. _____

7. What binomial coefficient gives the number of 3-element subsets that can be formed from a 10-element set?

7. _____

8. What is the 9th term of $(a + b)^{30}$?

8. _____

Chapter 10 Test, Form A

In 1 and 2, tell whether the problem involves an ordered or unordered collection of symbols, with or without repetition. You do not have to solve the problem.

1. There are one hundred students in the senior class who are participating in a dance contest. One prize will be given for first place, one for second, and one for third. In how many different ways can the three winners be chosen?

1. _____

2. A deli offers submarine sandwiches for lunch. Each is made from one of four different types of bread. The deli offers five different types of cheese, five different types of meat, and lettuce, tomatoes, onions, mayonnaise, mustard, and vinegrette for the sandwiches. You wish to determine how many types of sandwiches they offer, assuming a sandwich contains at least one type of cheese or meat.

2. _____

3. You have three assignments that are due tomorrow: one in history, one in mathematics, and one in English. Draw a possibility tree to determine in how many different orders you can do the assignments, assuming you work on only one assignment at a time and do not start the next one until the previous one is completed.

3.

4. Among integers from 1,000 through 9,999, how many have at least one even digit?

4. _____

In 5 and 6, evaluate the expression.

5. $P(15, 6)$

5. _____

6. $\binom{12}{7}$

6. _____

7. Show that $C(n, 1) = n$.

7. _____

_____

Chapter 10 Test, Form A   (page 2)

8. Jan wishes to buy three cans of soda for three co-workers. The soda machine offers cola, diet cola, root beer, lemon-lime, grape, and orange. In how many different ways can she choose the three cans of soda?

8. _____

In 9-11, determine how many 3-number combinations for a lock can be created using the numbers 0-49 for the given circumstance.

9. when repetition is allowed

9. _____

10. when repetition is not allowed

10. _____

11. when repetition is not allowed and the first number must be in the range 20-49

11. _____

12. A person going on a trip owns 11 shirts and needs to pack 5 of them. In how many ways can the traveler choose these 5 shirts?

12. _____

13. **a.** What is the seventh row of Pascal's triangle?

13. **a.** _____

_____

   b. Expand $(x + y)^7$.

b. _____

_____

_____

14. Find the fifth term in the expansion of $(x + 3y)^{10}$.

14. _____

15. If $\binom{n}{a} = \binom{n}{b}$ and $a \neq b$, what is true about a and b? Prove that your answer is correct.

15. _____

16. Write an expression using binomial coefficients that gives the number of subsets of a 6-element set.

16. _____

17. A certain chicken producer prides himself in the yellow color of his chickens. If the probability that any particular chicken is white is 0.3% and 20 chickens are selected for inspection, what is the probability that one or two of them will be white? (Assume that all chickens are either yellow or white.)

17. _____

Chapter 10 Test, Form B

In 1 and 2, tell whether the problem involves an ordered or unordered collection of symbols, with or without repetition. You do not have to solve the problem.

1. A computer randomly generates numbers between 0 and 9. You wish to determine how many different sequences of numbers are possible if 8 numbers are generated for each sequence.

1. _____

2. The president of a corporation wishes to choose 3 new members for an advisory council: one for marketing, one for production, and one for public relations. In how many different ways can these positions be filled if there are 12 people to choose from?

2. _____

3. An exercise manual suggests performing the following activities as warm-ups for weightlifting: stretching, push-ups, sit-ups, and jumping jacks. At least one of these activities needs to be done on a given day, but the final activity should always be stretching. Draw a possibility tree to determine the number of possible warm-up sequences.

3. _____

4. Among integers from 1,000 through 9,999, how many have no odd digits?

4. _____

In 5 and 6, evaluate the expression.

5. $P(12, 4)$

5. _____

6. $\binom{11}{8}$

6. _____

7. Show that $P(n, n) = n!$

7. _____

_____

Chapter 10 Test, Form B   (page 2)

8. Bruce plans to buy four pies for an upcoming office party.   8. _____
   The local bakery offers the following kinds of pies:
   chocolate cream, banana cream, pecan, lemon meringue,
   peach, apple, and caramel custard. In how many different
   ways can Bruce select four pics?

**In 9-11, determine how many 7-digit phone numbers can be
created using the digits 0-9 for the given circumstance.**

9. when repetition is not allowed   9. _____

10. when repetition is allowed and the first three digits must   10. _____
    be 7, 1, 4

11. when repetition is allowed but the digit 6 cannot be used   11. _____

12. A woman wins a vacation for four to Australia. If she has   12. _____
    twenty friends, in how many ways can she choose three to
    accompany her on the trip?

13. **a.** What is the sixth row of Pascal's triangle?   13. **a.** _____

                                                                       _____

    b. Expand $(x - y)^6$.   **b.** _____

                                                                       _____

                                                                       _____

14. Find the fourth term in the expansion of $(2x + y)^9$.   14. _____

15. If a and b are nonnegative integers and $a + b = n$, how   15. _____
    are $\binom{n}{a}$ and $\binom{n}{b}$ related? Prove that your answer is correct.

16. Write an exprcssion using binomial coefficients which   16. _____
    gives the number of nonempty subsets of a 7-element set.

17. The probability that any particular computer disk sold by   17. _____
    a certain supplier is defective is 2.4%. What is the
    probability that in a box of ten disks at least two are
    defective?

Chapter 10 Test, Cumulative Form

1. Given set $S = \{c, d, e, f\}$, find the number of 6-element collections that can be constructed (repetition is allowed).

   1. _____

2. How many different terms are in the expansion $(a + b + c + d)^8$?

   2. _____

3. How many 4-digit integers have digits which alternate odd-even-odd-even?

   3. _____

4. Find the derivative of the function k defined by $k(x) = 3x^2 + 4x$.

   4. _____

5. Calculate $C(12, 8) \cdot C(4, 2)$.

   5. _____

6. Find the total number of subsets that can be formed from a 5-element set.

   6. _____

7. Tell whether the function $f: x \to \lceil 2x \rceil$ is continuous on the given interval.

   a. $1 \leq x \leq 2$

   7. a. _____

   b. $1\frac{1}{2} < x < 2$

   b. _____

8. Show that $P(7, 3) = 3! \cdot C(7, 3)$.

   8. _____

   _____

9. The curator of an art gallery wishes to display 3 Picasso paintings, 2 Miro paintings, and 2 Chagall paintings side-by-side on one wall. If the Picassos must be placed together, how many different arrangements of the paintings are possible?

   9. _____

10. Let g be the function defined by $g(x) = x^2 + 7$. Calculate the average rate of change from $x = 1$ to $x = 3$.

    10. _____

11. Express $x^5 - 10x^4 + 40x^3 - 80x^2 + 80x - 32$ as the power of a binomial.

    11. _____

12. An athlete wants to try out for three track-and-field events: javelin throw, 100-meter dash, and shotput. Draw a possibility tree to represent all possible sequences of events for that athlete.

    12.

Precalculus and Discrete Mathematics © Scott, Foresman and Company

Chapter 10 Test, Cumulative Form   (page 2)

13. On the grid at the right, sketch the graph of an even
function h such that $\lim_{x\to\infty} h(x) = \infty$, and h has a relative
maximum at $x = 3$.

13.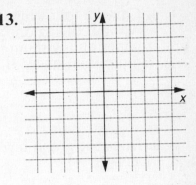

14. *True* or *false*? If a function has a relative minimum or
maximum at a point and the derivative exists at that
point, then the derivative of the function is zero at that
point.

14. _____

15. Express $\dfrac{\sqrt{5}}{2 - \sqrt{3}}$ as a fraction without radicals in the
denominator.

15. _____

16. An object is thrown upwards so that its height h (in feet)
t seconds after being thrown is given by $h(t) =$
$-16t^2 + 20t + 30$. What is the maximum height reached
by the object?

16. _____

17. Suppose $\pi < x < \frac{3\pi}{2}$, $\cos x = -\frac{1}{3}$, $0 < y < \frac{\pi}{2}$, and
$\sin y = \frac{2}{3}$. Find $\sin (x + y)$.

17. _____

Quiz for Lessons 11-1 Through 11-4

1. a. Can the following figure be drawn without lifting one's pen from the paper and without covering a line more than once? If so, show how.

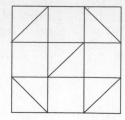

1. a. _____

b. Does the graph have an Euler circuit? Justify your answer.

b. _____

_____

_____

2. Write the adjacency matrix for the directed graph shown at the right.

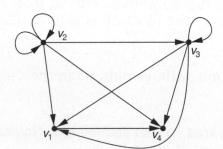

2. _____

3. *Multiple choice.* Which of the following graphs are connected?

3. _____

(a)
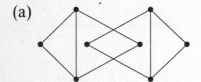

(b)
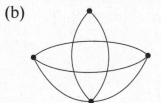

(c)
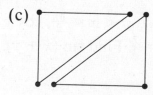

(d)
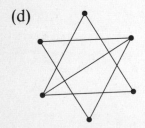

(e)
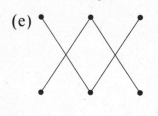

(f)
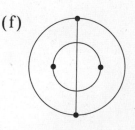

4. Draw a graph with six vertices of degrees 1, 2, 3, 4, 5, and 6, or show that no such graph exists.

4.

Quiz for Lessons 11-1 Through 11-4 (page 2)

5. In a class of 17 students, is it possible for each student to have exactly three friends in the class? Justify your answer.

5. _____

_____

_____

6. A computer manufacturer buys 72% of its memory chips from an outside supplier and makes the rest itself. Of the chips made by the supplier, 1% are defective, and of the chips that the computer manufacturer makes, 1.5% are defective.

   a. Draw a probability tree to represent the situation.

   6. a.

   b. What is the probability that if a defective chip is found, it was made by the outside supplier?

   b. _____

Chapter 11 Test, Form A

1. A map of houses and the streets between them is shown
below. A person is delivering pizza to houses A, B, C, D,
and E. Is it possible for the delivery person to leave the
pizza parlor, pass each house exactly once, and return to
the pizza parlor? Justify your answer.

1. _____

   _____

   _____

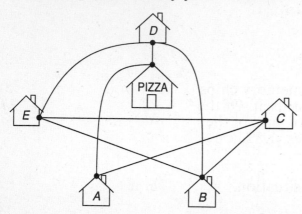

2. Draw a directed graph whose adjacency matrix is given
below.

2.

$$\begin{bmatrix} 2 & 1 & 1 \\ 1 & 0 & 2 \\ 0 & 1 & 0 \end{bmatrix}$$

3. Consider the graph at the
right. Identify an edge
such that when the edge is
removed, the graph is

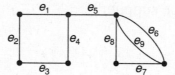

   a. simple.

3. a. _____

   b. not connected.

   b. _____

4. Draw a simple graph with six vertices of degrees 0, 1, 1, 2,
2, and 2.

4.

5. Does the complete graph of six vertices have an Euler
circuit? Justify your answer.

5. _____

      Precalculus and Discrete Mathematics © Scott, Foresman and Company

Chapter 11 Test, Form A   (page 2)

6. If the matrix shown below is the adjacency matrix of an undirected graph, find the values of x and y.

6. _____

$$\begin{bmatrix} 1 & 2 & x & 0 \\ 2 & 0 & 3 & 1 \\ 1 & y & 1 & 0 \\ 0 & 1 & 0 & 0 \end{bmatrix}$$

7. The adjacency matrix for an undirected graph is shown below. How many walks of length 3 go from v_2 to v_3?

7. _____

$$\begin{bmatrix} 1 & 0 & 1 \\ 0 & 2 & 1 \\ 1 & 1 & 0 \end{bmatrix}$$

8. Draw a simple graph with five vertices of degrees 1, 3, 3, 3, and 4, or show that no such graph exists.

8.

9. In a closed container, 15% of a certain liquid evaporates each minute into gaseous form and 20% of the gas condenses into liquid.

a. Draw a directed graph and label the edges with the appropriate probabilities to represent the situation.

9. a.

b. Find the fraction of the substance that is liquid after a long period of time.

b. _____

10. Use the graph shown at the right.

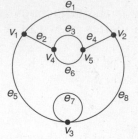

  a. Identify all vertices adjacent to v_1.

  b. Identify any parallel edges.

  c. The removal of which two edges would create a simple graph?

10. a. _____

b. _____

c. _____

11. a. Does a simple, connected graph with vertices of degrees 2, 2, 2, 2, and 4 contain an Euler circuit?

  b. Justify your answer.

11. a. _____

b. _____

12. a. Can the figure at the right be drawn without lifting one's pencil? If so, show how.

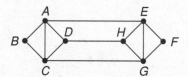

  b. Does the figure contain an Euler circuit? Justify your answer.

12. a. _____

b. _____

_____

13. Suppose that at a certain bank machine, 62% of the transactions are withdrawals and the rest are deposits. Suppose that the machine malfunctions during 1% of the withdrawals and during 1.2% of the deposits.

  a. Draw a probability tree to represent this situation.

13. a.

  b. What percentage of all malfunctions occur during deposits?

b. _____

Precalculus and Discrete Mathematics © Scott, Foresman and Company

Chapter 11 Test, Form B

1. A map is shown below. Mr. Smith is going to the airport to pick up his wife. Can he leave home, pick up his wife, and return home, stopping at the bank, the gas station, the grocery store, and the post office on the way, without passing any location more than once? Justify your answer.

1. _____

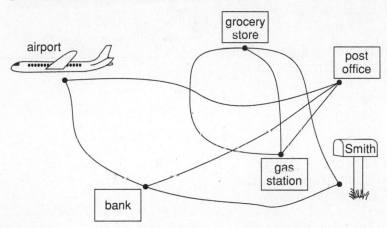

2. Draw a directed graph whose adjacency matrix is given below.

$$\begin{bmatrix} 1 & 1 & 1 \\ 0 & 2 & 1 \\ 1 & 0 & 0 \end{bmatrix}$$

2.

3. Consider the graph at the right. Identify an edge such that when the edge is removed, the graph is

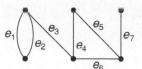

   a. simple.

3. **a.** _____

   b. not connected.

     b. _____

4. Draw a simple graph with five vertices of degrees 2, 3, 3, 4, and 4.

4.

5. Does the complete graph of seven vertices have an Euler circuit? Justify your answer.

5. _____

Chapter 11 Test, Form B   (page 2)

6. If the matrix below is the adjacency matrix of an
undirected graph, find the values of x and y.

6. _____

$$\begin{bmatrix} 0 & 4 & 1 & 2 \\ 4 & 1 & 0 & 3 \\ 1 & 0 & 4 & y \\ x & 3 & 0 & 2 \end{bmatrix}$$

7. The adjacency matrix for an undirected graph is shown
below. How many walks of length 4 go from v_3 to v_1?

7. _____

$$\begin{bmatrix} 0 & 1 & 2 \\ 1 & 0 & 0 \\ 2 & 0 & 3 \end{bmatrix}$$

8. Draw a simple graph with seven vertices of degrees 1, 1,
2, 3, 4, 5, and 5, or show that no such graph exists.

8.

9. In a closed container, 18% of a certain liquid evaporates
each minute into gaseous form, and 12% of the gas
condenses into liquid.

a. Draw a directed graph and label the edges with the
appropriate probabilities to represent the situation.

9. a.

b. Find the fraction of the substance that is gaseous after a
long period of time.

b. _____

Precalculus and Discrete Mathematics © Scott, Foresman and Company

Chapter 11 Test, Form B   (page 3)

10. Use the graph shown at the right.

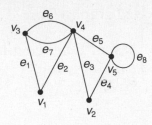

  a. Identify all vertices adjacent to v_4.

  b. Identify any parallel edges.

  c. The removal of which two edges would create a simple graph?

11. a. Does a simple, connected graph with vertices of degrees 2, 2, 2, 3, and 3 contain an Euler circuit?

  b. Justify your answer.

10. a. _____

  b. _____

  c. _____

11. a. _____

  b. _____

12. a. Can the figure at the right be drawn without lifting one's pencil? If so, show how.

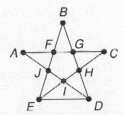

  b. Does it contain an Euler circuit? Justify your answer.

12. a. _____

  b. _____
  _____

13. In a certain town, 83% of the adults have a high school diploma. Of those adults with a high school diploma, 65% went to college, and 2% of the adults without a high school diploma also went to college.

  a. Draw a probability tree to represent this situation.

13. a.

  b. What is the probability that a randomly-selected college attendee in the town did not have a high school diploma?

  b. _____

Chapter 11 Test, Cumulative Form

1. Determine whether the undirected graph whose

adjacency matrix is $\begin{bmatrix} 2 & 2 & 2 \\ 2 & 1 & 0 \\ 2 & 0 & 4 \end{bmatrix}$ has an Euler circuit.

Justify your answer.

1. _____

2. Evaluate $\binom{100}{2}$.

2. _____

3. Use trigonometric identities to find the exact value of $\cos^2 15° - \sin^2 15°$.

3. _____

4. Draw a graph with five vertices of degrees 3, 3, 3, 3, and 4, or show that no such graph exists.

4.

5. When a fair coin is tossed seven times, which is more likely to result, three heads or four heads?

5. _____

6. How many edges does a complete graph with seven vertices have?

6. _____

7. Evaluate the infinite geometric series

$4 - 1\frac{1}{3} + \frac{4}{9} - \frac{4}{27} + \dots .$

7. _____

8. Find the total number of walks of length 3 which end at v_2 in the directed graph at the right.

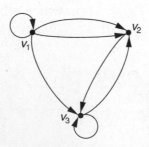

8. _____

9. In how many different ways can 3 math books, 2 history books, and 7 art books be arranged side-by-side on a shelf so that books on the same subject remain together?

9. _____

Precalculus and Discrete Mathematics © Scott, Foresman and Company

Chapter 11 Test, Cumulative Form   (page 2)

10. Find the total number of edges of a directed graph

whose adjacency matrix is $\begin{bmatrix} 2 & 1 & 3 \\ 0 & 0 & 2 \\ 3 & 2 & 1 \end{bmatrix}$.

10. _____

11. Show that $f(x) = 2x - 5$ and $g(x) = \frac{x}{2} + \frac{5}{2}$ are inverse functions.

11. _____

12. In a particular metropolitan area, 10% of the urban population shifts to the suburbs each year, while 7% of the suburban population shifts to the urban areas. Assume there is no other movement of people.

a. Draw a directed graph and label the edges with the appropriate probabilities to model the situation.

12. a.

b. What fraction of the population will be in the suburbs if this continues for a long period of time?

b. _____

13. How many terms are in the expansion of $(x + y + z)^7$?

13. _____

14. Do the following two diagrams represent the same graph? Why or why not?

14. _____

_____

_____

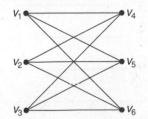
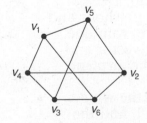

15. Find the quotient and the remainder when the polynomial $p(x) = x^4 - 2x^3 + 5x^2 - x + 6$ is divided by the polynomial $d(x) = x - 1$.

15. _____

Quiz for Lessons 12-1 Through 12-3

1. If $\vec{u} = (6, -7)$ and $\vec{v} = (3, 4)$, show that $\vec{u} + \vec{v}$ is parallel   **1.**
to the vector $\vec{w} = (-3, 1)$.

2. Given the vectors shown below, draw $\vec{u} - 2\vec{v}$.   **2.**

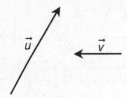

3. a. Give the endpoint of a vector which has polar   **3. a.** _____
representation $\left[4, \frac{\pi}{2}\right]$ and starts at the point $(-8, -1)$.

   b. Draw the vector.   **b.**

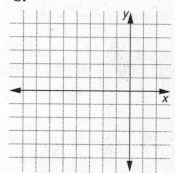

4. Find a vector equation for the line through the points   **4.** _____
(2, -5) and (5, -7).

5. a. An airplane's velocity is represented by [250, 152°],   **5. a.** _____
where the magnitude is measured in miles per hour and
the direction is in degrees counterclockwise from due   _____
east. Find the *x*- and *y*-components of this vector and
interpret them in terms of the motion of the airplane.   _____

    _____

   b. If the velocity given in part **a** is relative to the wind,   **b.** _____
and the wind's velocity is given by [35, 20°], find the
magnitude and direction of the plane's actual velocity
relative to the ground.

Precalculus and Discrete Mathematics © Scott, Foresman and Company

Quiz for Lessons 12-4 Through 12-6

1. Let $\vec{u} = (-1, 2)$, $\vec{v} = (0, 5)$, and $\vec{w} = (-4, -3)$. Compute $2\vec{u} \cdot (\vec{v} - \vec{w})$.

1. _____

2. Find x so that the vectors $\vec{s} = (x, 3, -1)$ and $\vec{t} = (x + 2, x, 6)$ are orthogonal.

2. _____

3. Find the center and radius of the sphere with equation $x^2 + y^2 + z^2 - 2x + 6y - 4z = 35$.

3. _____

4. Show that if $\vec{u} = (x, y)$ and $\vec{v} = (ky, -kx)$, $k \neq 0$, then $\vec{u}$ and $\vec{v}$ are orthogonal.

4.

5. Let $\vec{s} = (0, 2, -4)$ and $\vec{t} = (-2, 0, 1)$.

   a. Sketch $\vec{s}$ and $\vec{t}$.

5. a., c.

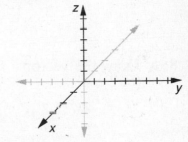

   b. Compute $\vec{s} \times \vec{t}$.

b. _____

   c. Add $\vec{s} \times \vec{t}$ to your sketch from part **a.**

   d. Find the measure of the angle between $\vec{s}$ and $\vec{t}$.

d. _____

Chapter 12 Test, Form A

In 1-3, let $\vec{u} = (-3, 2)$, $\vec{v} = (1, 4)$, and $\vec{w} = (-2, -5)$. Compute.

1. $|\vec{w}|$

1. _____

2. $\vec{u} \cdot (\vec{v} + \vec{w})$

2. _____

3. the angle between $\vec{u}$ and $\vec{w}$

3. _____

In 4-6, let $\vec{s} = (0, 2, 4)$ and $\vec{t} = (-1, -6, 3)$.

4. Are $\vec{s}$ and $\vec{t}$ parallel, perpendicular, or neither?

4. _____

5. Find $2\vec{s} - \vec{t}$.

5. _____

6. Find $\vec{s} \times \vec{t}$.

6. _____

7. Suppose $\vec{u}$ and $\vec{v}$ are vectors in 3-space such that $\vec{v} = k\vec{u}$ for some real number k. Prove that $\vec{u} \cdot \vec{v} = k|\vec{u}|^2$.

7.

8. a. Draw the vector $\vec{v}$ from the point $(1, -3)$ to the point $(6, 2)$.

8. a., d.

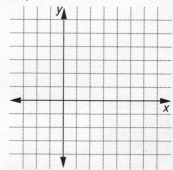

b. Find the component representation of $\vec{v}$.

b. _____

c. Find the polar representation of $\vec{v}$.

c. _____

d. Draw the standard position vector.

Precalculus and Discrete Mathematics © Scott, Foresman and Company

Chapter 12 Test, Form A   (page 2)

9. Draw the following vectors using the vectors shown at the right.

   a. $\vec{u} + \vec{v}$

   9. a.

   b. $\vec{u} - \vec{v}$

   b.

10. Draw the vector $\vec{q} = (2, 3, -2)$.

    10.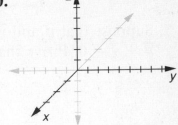

11. Write an equation for the sphere with center $(4, 2, -1)$ and radius 16.

    11. _____

12. Find an equation for the plane containing the point $(6, -1, -3)$ and perpendicular to the vector $(0, -2, 5)$.

    12. _____

13. Write parametric equations for the line through the point $P = (4, -1)$ and parallel to the vector $\vec{v} = (-3, 3)$.

    13. _____

14. Relative to the water, a boat is traveling at a speed of 12 knots in the direction 50° west of north. Because of the current, relative to land the boat actually is moving at a speed of 10 knots in the direction 40° west of north. Find the x- and y-components of the vector representing the boat's actual velocity relative to land.

    14. _____

15. Refer to Question 14. Find the speed and direction of the current.

    15. _____

Chapter 12 Test, Form B

In 1-3, let $\vec{u}$ = (-4, 2), $\vec{v}$ = (-1, -3), and $\vec{w}$ = (0, 5). Compute.

1. $|\vec{v}|$

1. _____

2. $\vec{v} \cdot (\vec{u} + \vec{w})$

2. _____

3. the angle between $\vec{v}$ and $\vec{w}$

3. _____

In 4-6, let $\vec{s}$ = (1, 3, 2) and $\vec{t}$ = (0, 2, 5).

4. Are $\vec{s}$ and $\vec{t}$ parallel, perpendicular, or neither?

4. _____

5. Find $\vec{s}$ - 2$\vec{t}$.

5. _____

6. Find $\vec{t} \times \vec{s}$.

6. _____

7. Suppose that $\vec{u}$ and $\vec{v}$ are vectors in a plane such that $\vec{u} + \vec{v}$ = 0. Prove that $\vec{u} \cdot \vec{v}$ = -$|\vec{u}|^2$.

7.

8. a. Draw the vector $\vec{v}$ from the point (-1, 2) to the point (3, 1).

8. a., d.

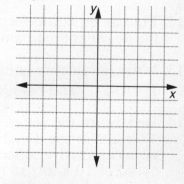

b. Find the component representation of $\vec{v}$.

b. _____

c. Find the polar representation of $\vec{v}$.

c. _____

d. Draw the standard position vector.

Chapter 12 Test, Form B   (page 2)

9. Draw the following vectors using the vectors shown at the right.

   a. $\vec{u} + \vec{v}$

9. **a.**

   b. $\vec{v} - \vec{u}$

   b.

10. Draw the vector $\vec{q} = (-1, 3, 1)$.

10.

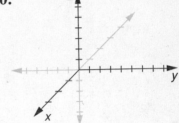

11. Write an equation for the sphere with center $(-3, 2, -1)$ and radius 25.

11. _____

12. Find an equation for the plane containing the point $(-2, 0, 5)$ and perpendicular to the vector $(8, -6, 3)$.

12. _____

13. Write parametric equations for the line through the point $P = (-3, -5)$ and parallel to the vector $\vec{v} = (-4, 2)$.

13. _____

14. A helicopter is traveling at a speed of 30 mph in the direction 66° north of east, but the wind pushes it so the helicopter actually is moving at a speed of 35 mph in the direction 20° west of north. Find the x- and y-components of the vector representing the helicopter's actual velocity relative to the ground.

14. _____

15. Refer to Question 14. Find the speed and direction of the wind.

15. _____

Chapter 12 Test, Cumulative Form

1. Let $\vec{u} = (-4, 2, 1)$, $\vec{v} = (0, 1, 3)$, and $\vec{w} = (2, 4, -2)$. Find $2\vec{u} \cdot (\vec{v} + \vec{w})$.

1. _____

2. Find the number of edges of a complete graph with five vertices.

2. _____

3. Write a vector equation for the line through $P = (-3, 2)$ and parallel to $\vec{v} = (-1, -4)$.

3. _____

4. Sketch the polar graph of the equation $r = 3$.

4.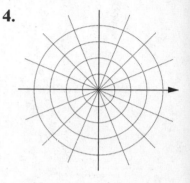

5. Find an equation for the sphere with center $(4, -2, 0)$ and radius 6.

5. _____

6. Does the graph at the right have an Euler circuit? If so, describe the circuit.

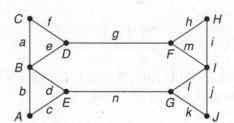

6. _____

_____

7. Find the measure of the angle between $\vec{s} = (4, 1, 1)$ and $\vec{t} = (-5, 2, 3)$.

7. _____

8. Find the third number in the tenth row of Pascal's triangle.

8. _____

   Precalculus and Discrete Mathematics © Scott, Foresman and Company

Chapter 12 Test, Cumulative Form   (page 2)

9. a. Give the magnitude and direction of the vector shown at the right.

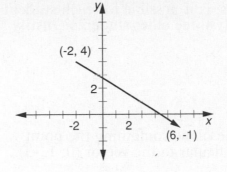

9. a. _____

b. Sketch the vector in standard position.

b.

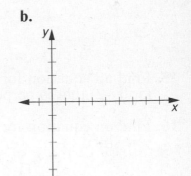

10. Write the adjacency matrix for the directed graph shown below.

10.

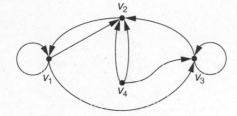

11. An airplane pilot wishes to achieve an actual speed of 500 mph in the direction 45° west of north. If a 40 mph wind is blowing from the north, what airspeed and compass bearing should the pilot maintain on the instrument panel?

11. _____

12. *Multiple choice.* $\cos(\alpha + \beta) = $ ___?___

(a) $\cos \alpha + \cos \beta$ (b) $\cos \alpha \cos \beta - \sin \alpha \sin \beta$
(c) $\cos \alpha \cos \beta + \sin \alpha \sin \beta$ (d) $\cos \alpha \sin \beta + \sin \alpha \cos \beta$

12. _____

13. Are $\vec{u} = (-6, 4)$ and $\vec{v} = (6, 10)$ parallel, perpendicular, or neither? Justify your answer.

13. _____

Chapter 12 Test, Cumulative Form   (page 3)

14. In a class of 23 students, is it possible for each student to shake hands with exactly three other students? Justify your answer.

14.
_____

15. Find an equation for the plane containing the point (5, 0, -2) that is perpendicular to the vector (0, 1, -3).

15. _____

16. Find an equation for the graph below as an image of $y = \sin x$.

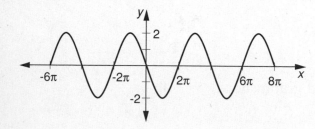

16. _____

Precalculus and Discrete Mathematics © Scott, Foresman and Company

Quiz for Lessons 13-1 Through 13-4

1. Use the following chart to construct a velocity-time graph. Estimate the distance traveled by the car over the 5-second interval by using left endpoints and by using right endpoints. Remember to label the axes of the graph.

1. _____

time (sec)	velocity (mph)
0	0
1	5
2	20
3	40
4	60
5	65

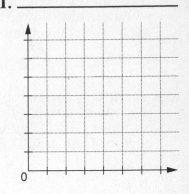

2. Evaluate the definite integral $\int_0^3 2x\, dx$.

2. _____

3. Express the area of the shaded region shown at the right by using integral notation, and evaluate the definite integral to find the area.

3. _____

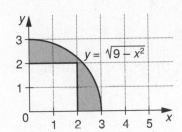

$y = \sqrt{9 - x^2}$

4. Use the properties of integrals to find the value of $\int_1^3 (4 + \ln x)\, dx - \int_1^3 \ln x\, dx$.

4. _____

5. Approximate the value of $\int_{-\pi/2}^{\pi/2} \cos x\, dx$ by using a Riemann sum with $\Delta x = \frac{\pi}{4}$ and $z_i =$ left endpoint of the ith subinterval.

5. _____

Continued **129**

Quiz for Lessons 13-1 Through 13-4 (page 2)

6. A capacitor is an electronic component that stores voltage
when current flows through it. The voltage V stored in a
capacitor is given by

$$V = \frac{1}{C} \int_{t_1}^{t_2} i(t)\, dt,$$

where C is the size of the capacitor (in farads) and $i(t)$ is
the rate of current flow (in amps) at various times t.
Suppose $C = .5$ farads and i is given by the following
current-time graph over the interval from 0 to 2 seconds.

6. _____

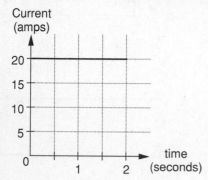

Find the voltage stored in the capacitor after 2 seconds.

Chapter 13 Test, Form A

1. Find the distance traveled over a 3-hour period by a train
with the following velocity-time graph.

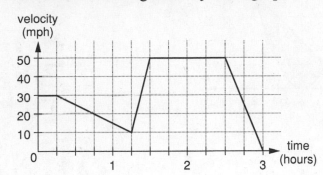

2. Given the graph below of $y = g(x)$, partition the interval
from 0 to 10 into five subintervals of equal length, Δx.

Estimate $\sum_{i=1}^{5} g(z_i) \, \Delta x$ when

a. z_i = the right endpoint of the ith subinterval.

2. **a.** _____

b. z_i = the left endpoint of the ith subinterval.

b. _____

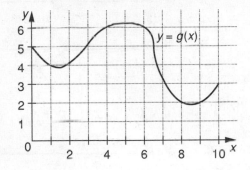

3. Express the area of the shaded
region using integral notation.

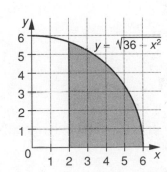

3. _____

Chapter 13 Test, Form A   (page 2)

4. Find the area of the shaded region shown at the right.

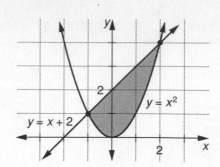

4. _____

In 5 and 6, find the exact value of the definite integral.

5. $\int_{-5}^{0} (-\sqrt{25 - x^2})\, dx$

5. _____

6. $\int_{-2}^{2} (2x - 2)\, dx$

6. _____

In 7 and 8, simplify the expression to a single integral.

7. $\int_{0}^{2} (3x^4 + 2x^2)\, dx + \int_{0}^{2} (3x^5 - 2x^2 + 1)\, dx$

7. _____

8. $2\int_{0}^{3} (6x + 1)\, dx + \int_{3}^{5} (12x + 2)\, dx$

8. _____

9. A car accelerates from 30 mph to 50 mph in 10 seconds. Assume that its acceleration is constant.

   a. Find its speed 3 seconds after it has begun accelerating.

9. a. _____

   b. Sketch a velocity-time graph.

   b.

   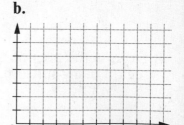

   c. Find the distance the car travels in the 10 seconds during which it accelerates.

   c. _____

Precalculus and Discrete Mathematics © Scott, Foresman and Company

Chapter 13 Test, Form A (page 3)

10. a. Use an integral to find the volume of the right circular cone generating by revolving the shaded region about the *x*-axis.

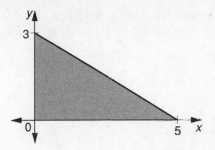

10. a. _____

b. Check your answer using the formula for the volume of a cone.

b. _____

11. A construction firm needs to fill in a parabolic trench 100 meters long. How much soil will the company need to completely fill the trench if its dimensions are 1 meter deep by 2 meters wide?

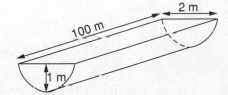

11. _____

Chapter 13 Test, Form B

1. Estimate the distance traveled by a missile over the 10
minute period depicted by the velocity-time graph below.

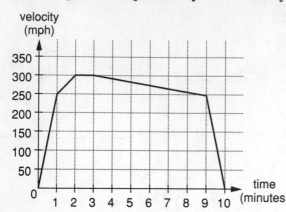

2. Given the graph of $y = g(x)$ below, partition the interval
from 0 to 10 into five subintervals of equal length, Δx.

Estimate $\displaystyle\sum_{i=1}^{5} g(z_i)\,\Delta x$ when

a. z_i = the right endpoint of the ith subinterval.

b. z_i = the left endpoint of the ith subinterval.

2. a. _____

b. _____

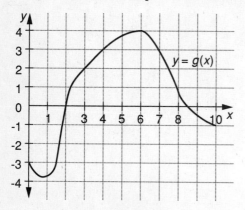

Precalculus and Discrete Mathematics © Scott, Foresman and Company

Chapter 13 Test, Form B   (page 2)

In 3 and 4, use the figure shown at the right.

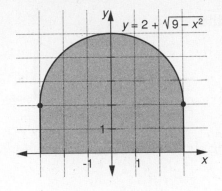

3. Express the area of the shaded region using integral notation.

4. Compute the area.

3. _____

4. _____

In 5 and 6, find the exact value of the definite integral.

5. $\int_{-4}^{3} (3x - 4)\, dx$

6. $\int_{2}^{7} (2x^2 - 4x + 2)\, dx$

5. _____

6. _____

In 7 and 8, simplify the expression to a single integral.

7. $3\int_{1}^{5} (x + 1)\, dx + \int_{5}^{10} (3x + 3)\, dx$

8. $\int_{-1}^{3} (x^5 + 3x^2 - 16)\, dx + \int_{-1}^{3} (2x^5 + x^3 - 3x^2)\, dx$

7. _____

8. _____

9. A car decelerates from 40 mph to 10 mph in 20 seconds. Assume that the deceleration is constant.

   a. Find the speed 6 seconds after it has begun decelerating.

   b. Sketch the velocity-time graph.

   c. Find the distance the car travels in the 20 seconds during which it decelerates.

9. a. _____

b.

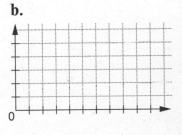

c. _____

Chapter 13 Test, Form B   (page 3)

10. a. Use an integral to find the volume of the right circular cone generating by revolving the shaded region about the *x*-axis.

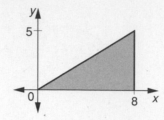

10. a. _____

b. Check your answer using the formula for the volume of a cone.

b. _____

11. How much water is needed to completely fill a parabolic birdbath 10 cm deep with a radius of 20 cm? (Turn the birdbath on its side so that it is generated by rotating the graph of $y = \sqrt{40x}$, $0 \le x \le 10$, about the *x*-axis.)

11. _____

Chapter 13 Test, Cumulative Form

1. To estimate the value of $\int_0^{10} (2 \ln x + e^{-x+2})\, dx$,
divide the interval into five equal subintervals. Let z_i be
the right endpoint of the ith subinterval and calculate the
Riemann sum.

1. _____

2. Use the properties of integrals to write the following
expression as a single integral.

$$\int_0^5 (x^2 + 3)\, dx - \int_0^4 (x^2 + 3)\, dx$$

2. _____

3. Find all vectors of length 3 in a plane that are orthogonal
to $\vec{z} = (2, 2)$.

3. _____

4. A car decelerates from 45 mph to a complete stop at a red
light in 12 seconds. The car's velocity over this interval is
given by $v(t) = -.458t^2 + 66$ ft/sec. Find the distance (in
feet) traveled during the decceleration.

4. _____

5. Rationalize the denominator of $\dfrac{8\sqrt{3}}{\sqrt{5} + \sqrt{3}}$.

5. _____

6. a. Express the area of the
shaded region using
integral notation.

b. Find the area.

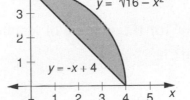

6. a. _____

b. _____

7. Is the vector $\vec{v} = (4, -2, 0)$ perpendicular to the plane M
defined by the equation $-2x + y = 39$? Justify your
answer.

7. _____

8. Calculate the value of
$$\int_{-1}^2 (2x^2)\, dx + \int_{-1}^2 (x + 1)\, dx.$$

8. _____

Chapter 13 Test, Cumulative Form   (page 2)

9. Use a truth table to prove that *~(p and q)* is equivalent to   **9.**
(~p) or (~q).

10. a. Draw the curve $y = \sqrt{9 - x^2}$ from $x = -3$ to $x = 3$.   **10. a.**

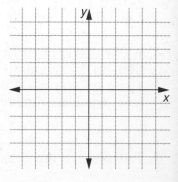

b. Use an integral to find the volume of the solid   **b.** _____
generated by revolving the curve in part **a** about the
x-axis.

c. Use the formula $V = \frac{4}{3}\pi r^3$ for the volume of a sphere to   **c.** _____
check your answer to part **b**.

11. A coin is dropped into a well 100 meters deep. The height
(in meters) of the coin above the water at time *t* seconds
is given by $h(t) = -5t^2 + 100$.

a. What is the instantaneous velocity of the coin at any   **11. a.** _____
time *t*?

b. At what time *t* does the coin hit the water?   **b.** _____

c. What is the velocity of the coin at the moment it hits   **c.** _____
the water?

    Precalculus and Discrete Mathematics © Scott, Foresman and Company

Chapter 13 Test, Cumulative Form   (page 3)

12. Suppose that $\vec{u} = (1, 2, -1)$ and $\vec{v} = (3, -4, 2)$. Compute.

    a. $\vec{u} \cdot \vec{v}$

    b. the angle between $\vec{u}$ and $\vec{v}$

12. a. _____

    b. _____

13. Show that the vectors $(-2, 4)$ and $(-6, 12)$ are parallel.

13. _____

Comprehensive Test, Chapters 1–13

1. If $f(x) = \sqrt{x^2 - 6}$ and $g(x) = \frac{1}{x}$, then the domain of $g \circ f$ is ___?___. 1. _____

    (a) $\{x: x \geq \sqrt{6}$ or $x \leq -\sqrt{6}\}$ (b) $\{x: x > \sqrt{6}$ or $x < -\sqrt{6}\}$
    (c) the set of all real numbers   (d) $\{x: x \geq \sqrt{6}\}$

2. Consider the statement: 2. _____

    If today is Sunday, then the department store is closed.
In which case would the statement be false?

    (a) *Today is not Sunday and the department store is closed.*
    (b) *Today is Monday and the department store is open.*
    (c) *Today is not Sunday and the department store is open.*
    (d) *Today is Sunday and the department store is open.*

3. If $0 < \theta < 90°$ and $\sin \theta = \cos 43°$, what is the value of θ? 3. _____

    (a) 43°   (b) -43°   (c) 47°   (d) -47°

4. Find the sum of the geometric series 4. _____

    $4 + 2 + 1 + \frac{1}{2} + \dots + \frac{1}{64}$.

    (a) 8   (b) $\frac{2^{10} - 1}{2^7}$

    (c) $\frac{2^9 - 1}{2^6}$ (d) $\frac{2^9 - 1}{2^8}$

5. Identify a factor of the polynomial 5. _____
$x^6 + 2x^5 - 4x^3 - 4x^2 + 5x + 6$.

    (a) $x - 1$ (b) $x + 1$
    (c) $x + 3$ (d) $x - 2$

6. The derivative g' of a function g is graphed at the right. On which of the following intervals is g increasing? 6. _____

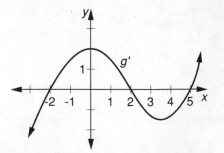

    (a) $-3 < x < 0$ (b) $2 < x < 5$
    (c) $x > 3$ (d) $0 < x < 2$

7. If $\tan \theta = \frac{12}{5}$, which of the following could be the value of $\csc \theta$? 7. _____

    (a) $\frac{12}{13}$ (b) $\frac{1}{5}$ (c) $\frac{13}{12}$ (d) $\frac{5}{12}$

              Precalculus and Discrete Mathematics © Scott, Foresman and Company

Comprehensive Test, Chapters 1–13 (page 2)

8. Find $\lim\limits_{n\to\infty} \dfrac{n}{2n+1}$.

8. _____

   (a) $\frac{1}{2}$ (b) 1   (c) $\frac{1}{3}$ (d) undefined

9. If $z = [2, 15°]$ and $w = [3, 20°]$ are two complex numbers, then $z \cdot w =$ ___?___.

9. _____

   (a) $[6, 35°]$ (b) $[6, 300°]$
   (c) $[5, 35°]$ (d) $[5, 300°]$

10. How many ways can five people be seated in a row?

10. _____

   (a) 5   (b) 10   (c) 120   (d) 24

11. What is the distance between $P = (-2, 4, 1)$ and $Q = (6, -3, -2)$?

11. _____

   (a) $3\sqrt{2}$ (b) $\sqrt{122}$ (c) $\sqrt{74}$ (d) $\sqrt{114}$

12. Evaluate the integral $\int_0^6 (3x^2 - 4x + 1)\, dx$.

12. _____

   (a) 1   (b) 85   (c) 32   (d) 150

13. Which of the following graphs has an Euler circuit?

13. _____

   (a)    (b)

   (c)    (d)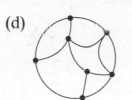

14. $\log_2 64 =$ ___?___

14. _____

   (a) 64   (b) 6   (c) 8   (d) 32

15. Solve for x. $\dfrac{x+1}{x-1} = \dfrac{2}{5}$

15. _____

   (a) 6   (b) $-\frac{7}{3}$ (c) $\frac{7}{3}$ (d) $\frac{1}{6}$

Comprehensive Test, Chapters 1–13 (page 3)

16. Which of the following is equal to $\sum_{k=1}^{n} (4 + k)^{k + 1}$?   16. _____

(a) $\sum_{j=0}^{n} (4 + j)^{j + 1}$ (b) $\sum_{j=0}^{n-1} (4 + j)^{j + 1}$

(c) $\sum_{j=1}^{n} (4 + k)^{k + 1}$ (d) $\sum_{j=0}^{n-1} (5 + j)^{j + 2}$

17. Given the graph of the function g at the right, on which of the following intervals is g' negative?   17. _____

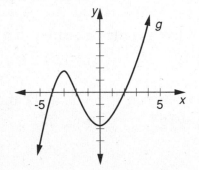

(a) $-5 < x < -3$ (b) $-3 < x < 0$
(c) $-2 < x < 2$ (d) $0 < x < 5$

18. Which pair of vectors are orthogonal?   18. _____

(a) $(4, 2, -1)$ and $(-2, -5, 1)$
(b) $(-6, 2, 0)$ and $(4, -1, 9)$
(c) $(-9, 5, -1)$ and $(1, 2, 1)$
(d) $(2, 4, 3)$ and $(4, 8, 6)$

19. Use the fact that $97 \equiv 5 \pmod{23}$ and $135 \equiv -3 \pmod{23}$ to find x when $97 + 135 \equiv x \pmod{23}$.   19. _____

(a) 8   (b) 15   (c) -15   (d) 2

20. If $f(x) = \frac{1}{3}x + 5$, then $f^{-1}(x) =$ ___?___.   20. _____

(a) $3x - 15$ (b) $3x - 5$

(c) $3x + 5$ (d) $\frac{1}{3}x - 5$

21. Let x be any real number. Then $\cos 2x$ is *not* equal to which of the following?   21. _____

(a) $\sin^2 x - \cos^2 x$ (b) $1 - 2 \sin^2 x$
(c) $2 \cos^2 x - 1$ (d) $\cos (-2x)$

22. If a coin were tossed 15 times, in how many different ways could exactly 4 tails results?   22. _____

(a) $\frac{15!}{4!}$ (b) $\frac{15!}{11!}$ (c) $\frac{15!}{11!4!}$ (d) $\frac{18!}{15!}$

          Precalculus and Discrete Mathematics © Scott, Foresman and Company

Comprehensive Test, Chapters 1–13 (page 4)

23. Which of the following integrals gives the area of the shaded region shown at the right?

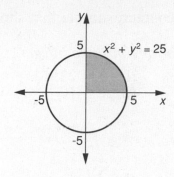

(a) $\int_0^5 (x^2 + y^2)\, dx$ (b) $\int_0^5 \sqrt{25 - y^2}\, dx$

(c) $\int_{-5}^5 \sqrt{25 - x^2}\, dx$ (d) $\int_0^5 \sqrt{25 - x^2}\, dx$

24. Which directed graph has the following adjacency matrix?

$$\begin{bmatrix} 0 & 1 & 1 & 0 \\ 1 & 0 & 1 & 0 \\ 0 & 0 & 0 & 1 \\ 0 & 1 & 1 & 0 \end{bmatrix}$$

(a)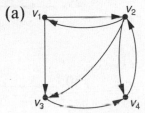

(b)

(c)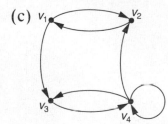

(d)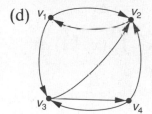

25. The zeros of a polynomial with real coefficients include $-2i$, 0, and $3i$. What is the smallest possible degree of the polynomial?

(a) 4   (b) 5   (c) 3   (d) 6

Comprehensive Test, Chapters 1–13 (page 5)

26. Which of the following is a counterexample that shows the following   26. _____
statement is false?

   $x^2 + x + 41$ is a prime for any positive integer x.

   (a) $x = 8$ (b) $x = 23$
   (c) $x = 41$ (d) $x = 10$

27. Which is equal to $\frac{1}{2} + \frac{1}{4} + \frac{1}{8} \ldots$?   27. _____

   (a) $\displaystyle\sum_{k=1}^{\infty}\left(\frac{1}{2k}\right)$ (b) $\displaystyle\sum_{k=2}^{\infty}\left(\frac{1}{k}\right)^2$

   (c) $\displaystyle\sum_{k=1}^{\infty}\left(\frac{k}{k+1}\right)$ (d) $\displaystyle\sum_{k=1}^{\infty}\left(\frac{1}{2}\right)^k$

28. What is the remainder when $p(x) = 4x^5 - 6x^3 - 5x^2 + 2x - 1$ 28. _____
is divided by $x - 7$?

   (a) $p(x - 7)$ (b) $p(7)$
   (c) $p(-7)$ (d) $p(x + 7)$

29. A simple graph can have which of the following?   29. _____

   (a) an isolated vertex   (b) a loop
   (c) two parallel edges   (d) two loops

30. Which of the following is *false*?   30. _____

   (a) $\displaystyle\int_{-2}^{2} 8(x^2 + x)\, dx = 8\int_{-2}^{2}(x^2 + x)\, dx$

   (b) $\displaystyle\int_{2}^{5} x^2(x - 1)\, dx = \int_{2}^{5} x^2\, dx \cdot \int_{2}^{5}(x - 1)\, dx$

   (c) $\displaystyle\int_{-4}^{2} 3x^4\, dx = \int_{1}^{2} 3x^4\, dx + \int_{-4}^{1} 3x^4\, dx$

   (d) $\displaystyle\int_{0}^{3} f(x)\, dx = \int_{-3}^{3} f(x)\, dx - \int_{-3}^{0} f(x)\, dx$

31. Find the values of x that satisfy $(x - 1)(x + 2) < 0$.   31. _____

   (a) $x < -2$ or $x > 1$ (b) $-2 \le x \le 1$
   (c) $-2 < x < 1$ (d) $x < 0$

                                   Precalculus and Discrete Mathematics © Scott, Foresman and Company

Comprehensive Test, Chapters 1–13 (page 6)

32. Suppose the function g is decreasing on the interval $-1 < x < 3$.   32. _____
Which of the following could be the graph of its derivative?

(a)
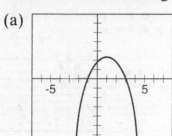

(b)
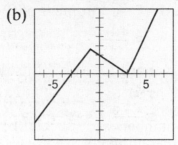

(c)
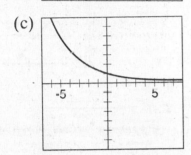

(d)
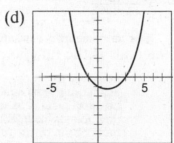

33. Which of the following is a polar equation for a circle?   33. _____

(a) $r = 3 + 2 \sin \theta$ (b) $r = 2 \sin \theta$

(c) $\theta = \frac{\pi}{2}$ (d) $r = 2^\theta$

34. Which expression is equal to $\tan x \cot x$ for all x in its domain?   34. _____

(a) $\sin^2 x - \cos^2 x$ (b) $\csc^2 x - \cot^2 x$

(c) $\frac{\sin^2 x}{\cos^2 x}$ (d) $\tan^2 x - \sec^2 x$

35. Which of the following vectors is parallel to $\vec{v} = (4, 3, -6)$?   35. _____

(a) $\left(\frac{1}{4}, \frac{1}{3}, -\frac{1}{6}\right)$ (b) $(-2, -1.5, 3)$

(c) $(8, 6, 12)$ (d) $(6, 0, 4)$

36. Identify the correct contrapositive of the statement: 36. _____
     If a figure is a square, then it is a rectangle.

(a) *If a figure is not a square, then it is not a rectangle.*
(b) *If a figure is a square, then it is not a rectangle.*
(c) *If a figure is not a rectangle, then it is not a square.*
(d) *If a figure is a rectangle, then it is not a square.*

37. How many terms are in the expansion of $(x + y + z)^6$?   37. _____

(a) $\binom{9}{3}$ (b) $\binom{6}{3}$ (c) $\binom{8}{3}$ (d) $\binom{8}{6}$

Comprehensive Test, Chapters 1–13 (page 7)

38. Which of the following is an irrational number?   38. _____

    (a) 0.10110111011110...
       (number of 1's increases)
    (b) 0.2020020200202002...
       (number of 0's is periodic)
    (c) $\sqrt{6} \cdot \sqrt{24}$
    (d) $\sqrt{-2}$

39. What is the range of the function $f: x \rightarrow |x|$ if its domain is the set   39. _____
of all real numbers?

    (a) the set of all real numbers
    (b) the set of positive real numbers
    (c) the set of nonnegative real numbers
    (d) the set of positive integers

40. On which of the following intervals is the function F defined by   40. _____
$F(x) = \lfloor x \rfloor$ continuous?

    (a) $0 < x \leq 1$
    (b) $0 \leq x \leq 1$
    (c) $1 \leq x < 2$
    (d) $1.5 < x < 2.5$

41. If $0 < \alpha < \frac{\pi}{2}$, $\cos \alpha = \frac{3}{5}$, $0 < \beta < \frac{\pi}{2}$, and $\sin \beta = \frac{5}{13}$, which is   41. _____
the value of $\cos (\alpha + \beta)$?

    (a) $\frac{3}{5} \cdot \frac{12}{13} - \frac{4}{5} \cdot \frac{5}{13}$
    (b) $\frac{3}{5} \cdot \frac{5}{13} + \frac{4}{5} \cdot \frac{12}{13}$

    (c) $\frac{3}{5} + \frac{5}{13}$
    (d) $\frac{3}{5} \cdot \frac{12}{13} + \frac{4}{5} \cdot \frac{5}{13}$

42. Let $p(x)$ and $q(x)$ be polynomials of degree m and n, respectively. If   42. _____
$m > n$, what is the highest possible degree of $h(x) = p(x) - q(x)$?

    (a) m (b) n (c) $m - n$ (d) $m \cdot n$

43. How many 4-digit even numbers can be formed using each of the   43. _____
digits 3, 7, 8, and 9 exactly once?

    (a) 24   (b) 6   (c) 64   (d) 256

44. Which of the following graphs is simple and connected?   44. _____

    (a)
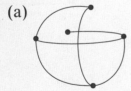
    (b)
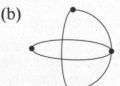

    (c)
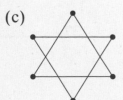
    (d)
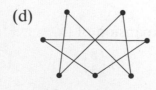

Comprehensive Test, Chapters 1-13 (page 8)

45. Given the list 5, 1, 4, 6, 2, 7. What is the list after the first pass of Quicksort? 45. _____

(a) 1, 4, 5, 2, 6, 7 (b) 1, 4, 5, 6, 2, 7
(c) 1, 2, 4, 5, 6, 7 (d) 1, 4, 2, 5, 6, 7

46. Suppose f is a function such that $f(t)$ is the velocity of an object moving along a straight line at time t. Which of the following gives the distance the object has traveled at time t? 46. _____

(a) $f'(t)$ (b) $f''(t)$

(c) $\int_0^t f'(x)\,dx$ (d) $\int_0^t f(x)\,dx$

47. Find $\lim\limits_{x\to 2^+} \dfrac{x^2 + 2x - 8}{x - 2}$. 47. _____

(a) ∞ (b) $-\infty$ (c) 6 (d) 1

48. The distance traveled by a car at time t is given by the formula $s(t) = 3t^2 - 6t$. Find the acceleration of the car at time $t = 5$. 48. _____

(a) 24 (b) 9 (c) 45 (d) 6

49. Let $\vec{u} = (2, -1)$ and $\vec{v} = (-7, 4)$. Find $3\vec{u} - 2\vec{v}$. 49. _____

(a) (-8, 5) (b) (20, -11)
(c) (9, -5) (d) (13, -7)

50. If the complex number $z = -2(\cos 15° + i \sin 15°)$, find z^6. 50. _____

(a) $64i$ (b) $-64i$ (c) 12 (d) -12

Answers for Quizzes and Tests

Included with the following answers are suggested point values for the items in each Chapter Test, Cumulative Test, and Comprehensive Test. These point values total 100 for each test. Instead of using the suggested point values, you may prefer to weight the test items differently by assigning your own values.

Quiz for Lessons 1-1 through 1-3

1. (a)
2. *There is a trapezoid that has no right angle.*
3.

p	q	~q	p or (~q)
T	T	F	T
T	F	T	T
F	T	F	F
F	F	T	T

4. (~p) or q
5. *If $x = \frac{1}{2}$, then $\frac{1}{x} = 2 \nleq 1$.*
6. $(\sqrt{3} + 5)^2 = 3 + 10\sqrt{3} + 25$
7. When either p or q is false or both are false.
8. (d)
9. False, only Middletown and Valley Ridge have $t > 40{,}000$, but both have 25 or more schools.
10. Answers may vary.

Quiz for Lessons 1-4 through 1-6

1. output
 1
 0
 1
 1
2. ~(p or ~(q and r))
3. *The sun sets and the wind doesn't die down.*
4. **a.** *If a boy is good, then he does fine.*
 b. *A particular boy is good, but he doesn't do fine.*
5. (b)
6. No; converse error
7. **a.** *If you have an English paper due, then you make popcorn.*
 b. Law of Transitivity
8. *If $a > 0$, then the graph of $y = ax^2 + bx + c$ opens upward. If the graph of $y = ax^2 + bx + c$ opens upward, then $a > 0$.*
9. DIFFERENT

Chapter 1 Test, Form A

(Items 1–12:   5 points each)
1. (d)
2. (b)
3. **a.** 12
 b. ∀ nonnegative real numbers a and b, $\sqrt{a}\sqrt{b} = \sqrt{ab}$

4. False
5. $5 < x$ and $(x < 7$ or $x = 7)$
6. *There is a symphony orchestra which doesn't employ a full-time tuba player.*
7. *I will not go to the concert or I will go to the restaurant.*
8. *If a student has a temperature higher than 99.6°, then (s)he shall not remain in school.*
9. *The president's speech is a success and the proposal is not approved.*
10. (c)
11. invalid, (d)
12. valid, (a)
(Items 13–19:   4 points each)
13. True;
 If n is even, then ∃ an integer k such that $n = 2k$.
 Then $n^2 + 1 = 4k^2 + 1 = 2(2k^2) + 1$. Since $2k^2$ is an integer, $n^2 + 1$ is odd.
14. False;
 When $n = 3$, $n^2 - n = 6$ is even, but n is not even.
15. False
16. False
17. △PQR is not a right △.
18. END
19. [~(p and q)] or ~q
(Items 20–21:   6 points each)
20.

p	q	p⇒q	~(p⇒q)
T	T	T	F
T	F	F	T
F	T	T	F
F	F	T	F

21. See below.

Chapter 1 Test, Form B

(Items 1–12:   5 points each)
1. (c)
2. (d)
3. **a.** $(2c - 3)(2c + 3)$
 b. ∀ real numbers a and b, $a^2 - b^2 = (a - b)(a + b)$

4. True
5. $(-2 < x$ or $-2 = x)$ and $x < 0$
6. *Some entrants are not adults and are not accompanied by a parent.*
7. *All people leave something on their plates when they eat.*
8. *There is a person who is eligible for enrollment at the university and who is not a high school graduate.*
9. *If the group has 10 or more people, then it will be charged a 15% gratuity.*
10. (b)
11. valid, (b)
12. invalid, (e)
(Items 13–19:   4 points each)
13. False;
 Let $m = 4$. Then m is even, but $\frac{m + 2}{2} = 3$ which is not even.
14. True;
 If a and b are odd, ∃ integers k and m such that $a = 2k + 1$ and $b = 2m + 1$.
 Then $a(b + 1) = (2k + 1)(2m + 1 + 1) = 2[(2k + 1)(m + 1)]$. Since $(2k + 1)(m + 1)$ is an integer, $a(b + 1)$ is even.
15. True
16. False
17. If $x^2 + y^2 = 0$, then $xy = 0$.
18. NO PROBLEM
19. [(~p) or q] and ~q
(Items 20–21:   6 points each)
20.

p	q	~q	p or (~q)
T	T	F	T
T	F	T	T
F	T	F	F
F	F	T	T

21.

p	q	p or q	~(p or q)	~p and ~q
T	T	T	F	F
T	F	T	F	F
F	T	T	F	F
F	F	F	T	T

21. See below.

Quiz for Lessons 2-1 through 2-3

1. $\{x: x \geq -12\}$
2. b is not a function because it maps 4 to more than one value—1979, 1981, 1983, 1985 and 1987.
3. a. $1979 \leq x \leq 1982$
 b. 5.0; 1982 or 1983
4. a. $\{y: 1 \leq y < 3\}$
 b. $2 \leq x \leq 4$
 c. No
 d. 1
5. a. $\ell(x) = \dfrac{500}{2x^2}$

 b. $S(x) = 4x^2 + \dfrac{1500}{x}$

 c. $x \approx 5.7$

Quiz for Lessons 2-5 through 2-6

1. a. $\dfrac{5}{2}, \dfrac{10}{3}, \dfrac{15}{4}, 4, \dfrac{25}{6}$

 b. increasing
 c. False
2. The limit of $f(x)$ as x approaches negative infinity is 8.

3.

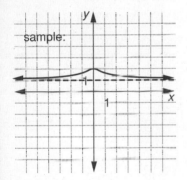

sample:

4. a.

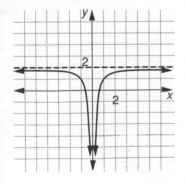

b. $\lim\limits_{x \to -\infty} f(x) = 2$, $\lim\limits_{x \to \infty} f(x) = 2$
 c. all real numbers except 0
5. $\dfrac{\ln 20}{.14} \approx 21.4$ years

Chapter 2 Test, Form A

(Items 1–10: 8 points each)
1. a. -8
 b. $x < 2$
2. $\{x: x > 0\}$, {all reals}
3. a. $x \leq -2$, $x > 0$
 b. $-2 \leq x < 0$
 c. -3
4. a. $\dfrac{8}{5}, \dfrac{8}{25}, \dfrac{8}{125}$
 b. 0
5. $x = 8$
6. $x = -5$
7. $\log 2 + \log x - \log y$
8. a. $x \leq -2$, $x \geq 1$
 b. $-2 \leq x \leq 1$
 c. -5
 d. 1
9. $1690.46
10. $\lim\limits_{x \to -\infty} g(x) = \infty$, $\lim\limits_{x \to \infty} g(x) = 0$
(Items 11–12: 10 points each)
11. $\lim\limits_{x \to -\infty} f(x) = 0$, $\lim\limits_{x \to \infty} f(x) = 0$
12. a. $\ell(x) = 12 - 2x$
 b. $w(x) = 9 - 2x$
 c. $V(x) = 4x(12 - 2x)(9 - 2x)$
 d.

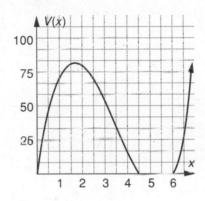

 e. $x \approx 1.7$

Chapter 2 Test, Form B

(Items 1–10: 8 points each)
1. a. $\dfrac{1}{3}$

 b. $x < \dfrac{1}{3}$

2. $\{x: x > -2\}$, {all reals}
3. a. $1 \leq x < 5$, $x > 5$
 b. $x \leq 1$
 c. -7
4. a. $2\dfrac{1}{3}, 2\dfrac{1}{9}, 2\dfrac{1}{27}$

 b. 2
5. $x = -3$
6. $x = 81$
7. $\log_{10} n - 2 \log_{10} m$
8. a. $1 \leq x \leq 3$
 b. $x \leq 1$, $x \geq 3$
 c. 3
 d. 3
9. $2523.04
10. $\lim\limits_{x \to -\infty} f(x) = 0$, $\lim\limits_{x \to \infty} f(x) = \infty$
(Items 11–12: 10 points each)
11. $\lim\limits_{x \to -\infty} g(x) = 0$, $\lim\limits_{x \to \infty} g(x) = 0$
12. a. $\ell(x) = 10 - 2x$

 b. $w(x) = 8 - 2x$
 c. $V(x) = x(10 - 2x)(8 - 2x)$
 d.

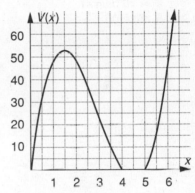

 e. $x \approx 1.5$

Chapter 2 Test, Cumulative Form

(Items 1–6: 7 points each)
1. a. $1790 \leq x \leq 1800$,
   $1810 \leq x \leq 1840$,
   $1850 \leq x \leq 1880$
 b. 1810, 1850
2. a. *9 is prime and 9 > 7.*
 b. No
3. *∀ positive integers x, ∃ a perfect square y such that $x = \sqrt{y}$.*
4. a. $p(x) \Rightarrow q(x)$
   $\sim q(c)$ for a particular c
   $\therefore \sim p(c)$
 b. Yes
5. a. $1 \leq x \leq 2$
 b. $-1 \leq x \leq 1$
 c. location: 2, value: -2
   location: $-1 < x < 1$,
   value: -1
6. $\{x: x > 0\}$

21.

p	q	$\sim p$ or q	p and $\sim q$	$\sim(p$ and $\sim q)$
T	T	T	F	T
T	F	F	T	F
F	T	T	F	T
F	F	T	F	T

(Items 7–12: 8 points each)
7. a.

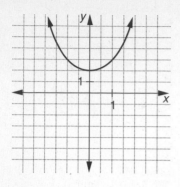

b. $\{y: y \geq 2\}$
c. even
8. $\lim\limits_{x \to -\infty} f(x) = \infty$, $\lim\limits_{x \to \infty} f(x) = -\infty$
9. $(\sim p)$ and q
10. (c)
11. 8
12. 7.4
(Item 13: 10 points)
13. a. $h = \sqrt{100 - x^2}$

b. $V = \dfrac{\pi}{3} \cdot x^2 \sqrt{100 - x^2}$

c.

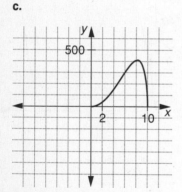

d. $x \approx 8.2$

Quiz for Lessons 3-1 through 3-3

1. $x = 729$
2. Yes
3. No
4. a. $(f \circ g)(x) = x^2 - 10x + 28$
b. No, $(g \circ f)(x) =$
$x^2 - 2 \neq (f \circ g)(x)$
5. False, because $(f \circ g)(x) =$
$x - 2 \neq x$
6. a. $1{,}500x + 1{,}000 \cos^{(2\pi x)}$
b.

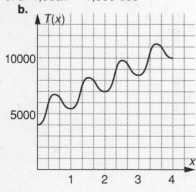

Quiz for Lessons 3-4 through 3-7

1. $\{x: b < x < c \text{ or } x > d\}$
2. a. 3
b. $2.56 < x < 2.57$
3. For $t > \log_5 .05$,

or $t > \dfrac{\log 20}{\log 2}$

4. True
5. $-3 < x < -1$ or $x > 5$
6. (a)
7.

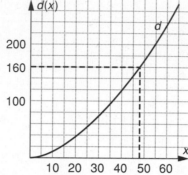

8. False, g is not continuous on
$a \leq x \leq b$.

9. $y = \pm 2$ or $\pm \sqrt{3}$

Chapter 3 Test, Form A

(Items 1–6: 5 points each)
1.

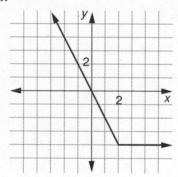

2. $(p \cdot q)(x) = x + 2$,
domain $= \{x: x \neq 2\}$
3. a. $(R \circ P)(t) = 50 - 18.4t$
b. minutes into climb
c. temperature outside aircraft t
minutes into climb

4. a. amplitude $= \dfrac{1}{2}$,

period $= 4\pi$,
phase shift $= 2\pi$
b. $y = \dfrac{1}{2} \sin \left(\dfrac{x - 2\pi}{2} \right)$, or

$y = -\dfrac{1}{2} \sin \dfrac{x}{2}$

5. a. $y = -3e^{2x}$
b. $y = -3e^{2(x+1)} + 2$
c. $\lim\limits_{x \to -\infty} y = 2$, $\lim\limits_{x \to \infty} y = -\infty$

6. a. $x < -2, -2 < x < 0,$
$0 < x < 5, x > 5$
b. $x < -2$ or $0 < x < 5$
(Items 7–13: 6 points each)
7. (c)
8. $-.7 < x < -.6$
9. (a), (b)

10. $x < -5$ or $\dfrac{5}{2} < x < \dfrac{10}{3}$

11. $x = -1$

12. $-\dfrac{28}{9} < k < -\dfrac{8}{9}$

13. $x = 3$
(Items 14–17: 7 points each)
14. $\approx .2$ km
15. No, because f is not 1–1 on
the set of real numbers
16. a. $g(1) = -3 < 0$
b. $g(3) = 5 > 0$
c. No, because g is not continuous on $1 \leq x \leq 3$, and
its graph does not cross the
x-axis on $1 \leq x \leq 3$
17. $|x - .043| \leq .001|$, when x is
the actual gap

Chapter 3 Test, Form B

(Items 1–6: 5 points each)
1.

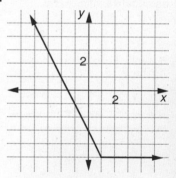

2. $\left(\dfrac{k}{m} \right)(x) = x - 2$,

domain $= \{x: x \neq -3\}$
3. a. $(P \circ n)(x) = -\dfrac{x^2}{10} + 42x - 3600$

b. price of each TV
c. monthly profit when price is x
4. a. amplitude $= 2$
period $= 2\pi$

phase shift $= \dfrac{\pi}{4}$

b. $y = 2 \cos \left(x - \dfrac{\pi}{4} \right)$

5. a. $y = \dfrac{1}{3} \ln \left(-\dfrac{x}{2} \right)$

b. $y = \dfrac{1}{3} \ln \left(-\dfrac{x - 2}{2} \right) - 3$

c. $\lim\limits_{x \to -\infty} y = \infty$, $\lim\limits_{x \to \infty} y$ is not defined
6. a. $x < -3, -3 < x < 0,$
$0 < x < 6, x > 6$
b. $-3 \leq x \leq 0$ or $x \geq 6$

(Items 7–13: 6 points each)
7. (c)

8. $1.0 < x < 1.1$

9. (c)

10. $-7 < x < \frac{1}{2}, \frac{1}{2} < x < 2, x > 2$

11. $n = \pm\sqrt{6}$

12. $y \geq 3$ or $y \leq \frac{1}{3}$

13. $x = 1, 2$

(Items 14–17: 7 points each)

14. $\approx .128$ km

15. No, because f is not 1–1 on the set of real numbers

16. a. 1
   b. -1
   c. No, $y = \tan x$ is not continuous on $\frac{\pi}{4} < x < \frac{3\pi}{4}$

17. $|x - .8| \leq .005$, when x is the actual diameter

Chapter 3 Test, Cumulative Form

(Items 1–4: 5 points each)
1. a. 0, 6
   b. -2
   c. $-2 < y \leq 3$

2. (c)

3. $\forall x > 2, (g \circ f)(x) = e^{\ln(x-2)} + 2 = (x - 2) + 2 = x,$
   $\forall x, (f \circ g)(x) = \ln(e^{x+2-2}) = \ln e^x = x$

4. Robert is not 16 years old or has not passed Driver's Education; by modus tollens and De Morgan's Law

(Items 5–15: 6 points each)
5. a. negative
   b. positive
   c. zero

6. $g(x) = 4 \cdot 2^{-x^2} + 2$

7. 6

8. ln 3, ln 8

9. 12 or $\frac{2}{3}$

10. $\left\{y: y \leq \frac{9}{2}\right\}$

11. $x < -4$ or $x > 7$

12. 0, 2.2, 6.8

13. 0

14. No

15. $I > 1$ watt/m²

(Items 16–17: 7 points each)

16. $f(x) = -\frac{x^2}{100} + 8x - 1000$

17. False;
   Let $n = 2$ and $m = 3$. Then m is odd, but $mn = 6$ is not odd.

Comprehensive Test, Chapters 1–3

(Items 1–25: 4 points each)
1. (a)
2. (b)
3. (d)
4. (b)
5. (a)
6. (c)
7. (c)
8. (a)
9. (d)
10. (c)
11. (d)
12. (b)
13. (a)
14. (b)
15. (a)
16. (d)
17. (c)
18. (a)
19. (b)
20. (c)
21. (d)
22. (b)
23. (b)
24. (d)
25. (b)

Quiz for Lessons 4-1 through 4-3

1. 7
2. real number division
3. 51
4. $2x^3 - 50x = 2x(x - 5)(x + 5)$
5. sample: $n = 167, d = 7$
6. 3
7. a. 3, 8, 13, 18, 23
   b. $a_n \equiv 3 \pmod 5$
8. Yes, because $10 \cdot 0 + 9 \cdot 6 + 8 \cdot 7 + \ldots + 2 \cdot 0 + 3 \equiv 0 \pmod{11}$
9. True. If 2 is a factor of n and 5 is a factor of m, then $\exists k$ and ℓ (integers) such that $n = 2k$ and $m = 5\ell$. Thus, $mn = (5\ell)(2k) = 10\ell k$. Since ℓk is an integer, 10 is a factor of mn.

Quiz for Lessons 4-4 through 4-6

1. a. $r(x) = -6x - 5$
   b. 1
2. a. $r(x) = 0$
   b. undefined
3. $q(x) = 2x^2 - 3x + 24$
   $r(x) = -128$
4. $x + 5, x - 3$
5. $(((6x - 3)x + 5)x + 6)x$
6. a. $x + 5$
   b. $3x^3 - 5x^2 + x - 5$
   c. 0
7. A polynomial of degree 3 can have no more than 3 zeros.
8. 185

Chapter 4 Test, Form A

(Items 1–4: 5 points each)
1. a. 416
   b. 16
   c. $10,000 = 24 \cdot 416 + 16$
2. sample: $n = 19, d = 5$
3. $3x^2 + 22x + 7 = (3x + 1)(x + 7)$
4. $q(x) = -3x^2 + 9x + 4$
   $r(x) = -2$

(Items 5–16: 6 points each)
5. True; The graph of a sixth degree polynomial function can cross the x-axis no more than 6 times. The graph does not violate this requirement.
6. True;
   $n^3 + 3n^2 + 2n = n(n + 1)(n + 2)$
   If n is an integer, then by the Quotient-Remainder Theorem $\exists$ integers q and r with $0 \leq r < 3$ such that $n = 3q + r$.
   If $r = 0$, then $n = 3q$, so n is divisible by 3.
   If $r = 1$, then $n = 3q + 1$, so $n + 2 = 3q + 3 = 3(q + 1)$ which is divisible by 3.
   If $r = 2$, then $n = 3q + 2$, so $n + 1 = 3q + 3 = 3(q + 1)$ which is divisible by 3.
   $\therefore$ in any case, $n(n + 1)(n + 3)$ is divisible by 3.
7. False;
   Let $a = 3, b = 7, c = 5$. Then a divides $b + c = 12$, but a divides neither b nor c.
8. 27
9. 11101_2
10. 5
11. $x \equiv 4 \pmod{11}$
12. 329
13. $2^3 \cdot 3 \cdot 5 \cdot 17$
14. $3(x + 2)(x - 2)(x^2 + 3)$
15. $x = \frac{5}{3}$ or $-\frac{1}{2}$
16. 3
(Item 17: 8 points)
17. a. Suppose there is a smallest negative integer.
   b. Let that integer be n. Then $n - 1$ is also a negative integer. But $n - 1 < n$, contradicting the claim that n is the smallest negative integer. Therefore, the assumption must be false; there is no smallest negative integer.

Chapter 4 Test, Form B

(Items 1–4: 5 points each)
1. a. 312
   b. 4
   c. $2500 = 8 \cdot 312 + 4$
2. sample: $n = 19, d = 4$
3. $4x^2 + 30x + 14 = (4x + 12)(x + 17)$

4. $q(x) = 2x^2 - 5x - 7$
$r(x) = x + 1$
(Items 5–16: 6 points each)

5. False; The graph of a fourth-degree polynomial function can cross the x-axis in no more than four places.

6. False; Let $n = 2$, then $2^3 - 2 = 6$ which is not divisible by 4.

7. True;
If a divides b and c, then $\exists$ integers k and ℓ such that $b = ak$ and $c = a\ell$. Thus, $b - c = ak - a\ell = a(k - \ell)$. Since $k - \ell$ is an integer, a divides $b - c$.

8. 45

9. 100101_2

10. 7

11. $x \equiv 3 \pmod{13}$

12. 368

13. $2^2 \cdot 5 \cdot 241$

14. $(x + 3)(x - 3)(x^2 + 1)$

15. $\frac{1}{2}$, -5

16. 2221

(Item 17: 8 points)

17. a. Assume there is a largest integer divisible by 3.
b. Let it be n. Then $\exists$ an integer k such that $n = 3k$. Then $n + 3$ is also an integer divisible by 3. But $n + 3 > n$, contradicting the assumption n is the largest integer divisible by 3. $\therefore$ the assumption is false; there is no largest integer divisible by 3.

Chapter 4 Test, Cumulative Form

(Items 1–16: 4 points each)

1. $2x^4 - 5x^3 + 7x^2 + 5x + 7$

2. a. -2
b. 3

3. 8

4. $\exists x$ such that $x + 1 \geq x + 2$ or $x = -x$

5. a. 20
b. 20
c. $500 = 20 \cdot 24 + 20$

6. 18.36

7. $\approx \$.28$

8. Students 2, 8, 20 (student n where $n = 14 \pmod 6$)

9. $g(x) = -|x - 4| - 2$

10. $q(x) = x^3 - 2x^2 + 4x - 8$, $r(x) = 0$

11. rel. min. value $\approx$ -20.7 at $x \approx 3.3$, rel. max value ≈ 12.6 at $x \approx -.7$

12. 52

13. $(f \cdot g)(x) = x^2 - 1 - \dfrac{2}{x^2}$

14. Limits as $x \to \pm\infty$ do not exist because values oscillate between 1 and -1.

15. True, because $53 - 18 = 35$ and 7 is a factor of 35

16. $\forall x \geq 0$, $f(g(x)) =$
$((x - 5)^{\frac{4}{3}})^{\frac{3}{4}} + 5 =$
$x - 5 + 5 = x.$

$\forall x \geq 5$, $g(f(x)) =$
$((x + 5)^{\frac{3}{4}} - 5)^{\frac{4}{3}} = (x^{\frac{3}{4}})^{\frac{4}{3}} = x.$

(Items 17–19: 12 points each)

17. p and $((\sim p)$ or $q)$
T
F
F
F

18. True;
If a is a factor of b and c is a factor of d, then $\exists$ integers k and ℓ such that $b = ak$ and $d = c\ell$. Thus, $bd = (ak)(c\ell) = ac(k\ell)$. Since $k\ell$ is an integer, ac is a factor of bd.

19. a. Assume that there is a largest integer that is an integer power of 10.
b. Let n be this integer. Then $10n$ is an integer that is an integer power of 10. (This is because $\exists$ an integer k such that $n = 10^k$, so $10n = 10^{k+1}$.) But $10n > n$, contradicting the assumption that n is the largest integer power of 10. Therefore, the assumption must be false; there is no largest integer that is an integer power of 10.

Quiz for Lessons 5-1 through 5-3

1. $\dfrac{10 + \sqrt{2}}{49}$

2. $\dfrac{1}{x - 5}$, $x \neq -2, -1, 0, 5$

3. (c)

4. a. $\dfrac{2}{n}$

b. $\dfrac{1}{n + 3}$

c. $\dfrac{3n + 6}{n(n + 3)}$

5. sample: $\sqrt[4]{2}$

6. a.

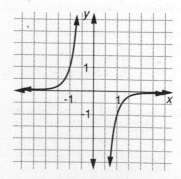

b. $\lim_{x \to -\infty} f(x) = \lim_{x \to \infty} f(x) = 0$

c. $\lim_{x \to 0^+} f(x) = -\infty$, $\lim_{x \to 0^-} f(x) = \infty$

7. Assume $\sqrt{19}$ is rational. Thus, $\exists$ integers a, $b(b \neq 0)$ such that $\sqrt{19} = \dfrac{a}{b}$ and a and b have no common factors. $\sqrt{19} = \dfrac{a}{b} \Rightarrow$ $19 = \dfrac{a^2}{b^2} \Rightarrow 19b^2 = a^2$, so a^2 is divisible by 19. By the theorem that says if n^2 is divisible by a prime p then n is divisible by p, a is divisible by 19. Thus, $\exists$ integer k such that $a = 19k$. $19b^2 = a^2 = (19k)^2 \Rightarrow b = 19k^2$, so b^2 is divisible by 19. Therefore, b is divisible by 19. Thus, both a and b are divisible by 19, contradicting the statement that they have no common factors. Thus, the assumption is false and $\sqrt{19}$ is irrational.

Quiz for Lessons 5-4 through 5-6

1. sample: $f(x) = x^{\frac{3}{2}}$

2. a. $\lim_{x \to -\infty} g(x) = \lim_{x \to \infty} g(x) = 0$

b. $\lim_{x \to -6^+} g(x) = \infty$, $\lim_{x \to -6^-} g(x) = -\infty$

c. essential discont. at $x = -6$

3. $f(x) = \dfrac{(-x + 2)(x - 3)}{x - 3}$

4.

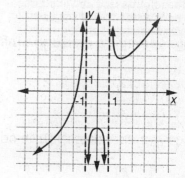

5. a. $y = 1$
b. ∞

6. $\dfrac{2\sqrt{3}}{3}$

7. a. $x = k\pi$, where k is an integer
b. essential

Chapter 5 Test, Form A

(Items 1–3: 5 points each)

1. a. $\dfrac{(x - 4)(x - 1)}{(x + 6)(x + 1)}$

b. $x \neq -6, -1$

2. a. $\dfrac{3(x + 5)}{2(x + 7)^2}$

b. $x \ne -7, 9$

3. a. False

b. $x = 4$

c. $x = 3$

(Item 4:   12 points)

4. Assume $\sqrt{5}$ is rational. Then $\exists$ integers a and b ($b \ne 0$) such that $\sqrt{5} = \dfrac{a}{b}$, and a and b have no common factors. $5 = \dfrac{a^2}{b^2} \Rightarrow$

$5b^2 = a^2$. By the theorem that states if n^2 is divisible by a prime p, then n is divisible by p, a is divisible by 5 since a^2 is. $\therefore \exists$ an integer k such that $a = 5k$. Thus, $5b^2 = a^2 = (5k)^2 = 25k^2 \Rightarrow b^2 = 5k^2$. Since 5 is a factor of b^2, it is a factor of b. This contradicts the statement that a and b have no common factor. Therefore the assumption is false and $\sqrt{5}$ is irrational.

(Items 5–14:   6 points each)

5. $h = \dfrac{fs}{s + v}$

6. $-\dfrac{10 + 12\sqrt{5}}{31}$

7. a. $\left\{x : x \ne -\dfrac{2}{3}\right\}$

b. essential discont. at $x = -\dfrac{2}{3}$

c. vert: $x -\dfrac{2}{3}$,

horiz: $y = \dfrac{4}{3}$

d. $\left(\dfrac{1}{4}, 0\right), \left(0, -\dfrac{1}{2}\right)$

e.

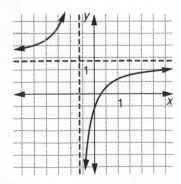

8. $z = 2$ or $\dfrac{5}{13}$

9. $\lim\limits_{x \to 4^+} \dfrac{1}{x - 4} = \infty$

10. a. $\lim\limits_{x \to 4^-} f(x) = \infty$;

$\lim\limits_{x \to 4^+} f(x) = -\infty$

b. $\lim\limits_{x \to -\infty} f(x) = \lim\limits_{x \to \infty} f(x) = 3$

11. $y = x + 3$

12. $\sqrt{3}$

13. $\dfrac{c}{a}$

14.

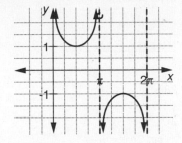

(Item 15:   13 points)

15. No; for example, $\sqrt{12}$ and $\sqrt{3}$ are irrational, but the quotient is rational:

$\dfrac{\sqrt{12}}{\sqrt{3}} = \sqrt{4} = 2$

Chapter 5 Test, Form B

(Items 1–3:   5 points each)

1. a. $\dfrac{2x + 13}{(x - 5)(x + 5)}$

b. $x \ne \pm 5$

2. a. $\dfrac{5(x \pm 2)}{2(x \pm 3)^2}$

b. $x \ne -3, 5$

3. a. True

b. sample: 1

c. sample: $\sqrt[4]{2}$

(Item 4:   12 points)

4. Assume $\sqrt{3}$ is rational. Then $\exists$ integers a, b ($b \ne 0$) with no common factor such that $\sqrt{3} = \dfrac{a}{b} \Rightarrow 3 = \dfrac{a^2}{b^2} \Rightarrow 3b^2 = a^2 \Rightarrow 3$ is a factor of a^2. By the theorem which states that if a prime is a factor of n^2, then it is a factor of n, 3 is a factor of $a \Rightarrow \exists$ integer k such that $a = 3k \Rightarrow 3b^2 = a^2 = (3k)^2 = 9k^2 \Rightarrow b^2 = 3k^2 \Rightarrow 3$ is a factor of $b^2 \Rightarrow 3$ is a factor of b. But this contradicts the statement that a and b have no common factor. $\therefore$ the assumption is false and $\sqrt{3}$ is irrational.

(Items 5–14:   6 points each)

5. $\dfrac{R_1R_2 + R_1R_3 + R_2R_3}{R_1 + R_2}$

6. $2\sqrt{6} - 3\sqrt{2}$

7. a. $\left\{x : x \ne -\dfrac{1}{4}\right\}$

b. essential discont. at $x = -\dfrac{1}{4}$

c. horiz: $y = \dfrac{1}{2}$,

vert: $x = -\dfrac{1}{4}$

d. $(0, -3), \left(\dfrac{3}{2}, 0\right)$

e.

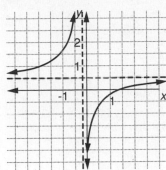

8. $z = 2$ or 3

9. $\lim\limits_{x \to -2^-} \dfrac{1}{(x + 2)^2} = \infty$

10. a. $\lim\limits_{x \to 2^-} f(x) = -\infty$;

$\lim\limits_{x \to 2^+} f(x) = \infty$

b. $\lim\limits_{x \to -\infty} f(x) = 1; \lim\limits_{x \to \infty} f(x) = 2$

11. $y = 3x - 9$

12. $\dfrac{2\sqrt{3}}{3}$

13. $\dfrac{c}{b}$

14.

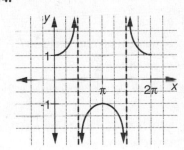

(Item 15:   13 points)

15. False;

For example, $\sqrt{3}$ is irrational and $\sqrt{3}$ is real, but the product is rational: $\sqrt{3} \cdot \sqrt{3} = 3$.

Chapter 5 Test, Cumulative Form

(Items 1–3:   4 points each)

1. a. ∞

b. $y = b$

2. The graph of h has a hole (removable discontinuity) at $(7, 98)$, but g doesn't; otherwise, they're the same.

3. ∞

(Items 4–13: 5 points each)
4. $2(4x + 7)(x - 1)(x - 5)$
5. -2.29
6. rational
7. $\dfrac{3x + 1}{(x + 5)(x - 2)}$; $x \neq -5, 2$
8. $\dfrac{-8\sqrt{3} - 6}{13}$
9. $3x^3 - 8x^2 + 5x + 9 =$
$(x - 2)(3x^2 - 2x + 1) + 11$
10. 3 mph
11. a. 4
    b. 0
12. $(f \circ g)(x) = \dfrac{5x}{1 + 2x}$
13. A $>$ = B OR B $>$ = C
(Items 14–16: 9 points each)
14. rel. min.: $\approx$ -.2 at $x \approx$ -.4,
rel. max: $\approx$ .5 at $x \approx$ .5
15. $q = 38$, $r = 10$
16. $x \leq$ -34 or $x \geq 71$
(Item 17: 11 points)
17. Assume $\sqrt{17}$ is rational. Then
$\exists$ integers a, b ($b \neq 0$) with no
common factor such that 17 is
a factor of a (by a theorem) $\Rightarrow$
$\exists$ integer k such that $a = 17k$
$\Rightarrow 17b^2 = a^2 = (17k)^2 \Rightarrow b^2 =$
$17k^2 \Rightarrow 17$ is a factor of $b^2 \Rightarrow$
17 is a factor of b. This con-
tradicts the assumption that a
and b have no common fac-
tors. $\therefore$ the assumption is false
and $\sqrt{17}$ is irrational.

Quiz for Lessons 6-1 through 6-3

1. a. Yes
    b. {all real numbers except $\dfrac{k\pi}{2}$
       when k is an integer}
2. Sample: At $x = \dfrac{\pi}{2}$, $2 \sin x = 2$
but $\sin 2x = \sin \left(2\left(\dfrac{\pi}{2}\right)\right) =$
$\sin \pi = 0$
3. $-2\sqrt{2}$
4. $\dfrac{\sqrt{2} - \sqrt{6}}{4}$
5. left side $=$
$\dfrac{1}{\sin x \cos x} - \dfrac{\cos x}{\sin x} =$
$\dfrac{1 - \cos^2 x}{\sin x \cos x} = \dfrac{\sin^2 x}{\sin x \cos x} =$
$\dfrac{\sin x}{\cos x} = \tan x$
6. right side $=$
$\dfrac{\cos (5x + x)}{\sin x \cos x} =$
$\dfrac{\cos 5x \cos x - \sin 5x \sin x}{\sin x \cos x} =$
$\dfrac{\cos 5x}{\sin x} - \dfrac{\sin 5x}{\cos x}$

Quiz for Lessons 6-4 through 6-6

1. $\cos \alpha \cos \beta - \sin \alpha \sin \beta$
2. $\dfrac{\tan a - \tan b}{1 + \tan a \tan b}$
3. $2 \sin x \cos x$
4. $\sin \left(x + \dfrac{\pi}{6}\right) =$
$\dfrac{\sqrt{3} \sin x + \cos x}{2}$
5. $\dfrac{240}{289}$
6. $\dfrac{1}{2}$
7. $\dfrac{\sin 2\theta}{1 + \cos 2\theta} =$
$\dfrac{2 \sin \theta \cos \theta}{1 + \cos^2 \theta - \sin^2 \theta} =$
$\dfrac{2 \sin \theta \cos \theta}{\cos^2 \theta + (1 - \sin^2 \theta)} =$
$\dfrac{2 \sin \theta \cos \theta}{2 \cos^2 \theta} = \dfrac{\sin \theta}{\cos \theta} =$
$\tan \theta$
domain: { all real numbers ex-
cept $\dfrac{(2k + 1)\pi}{2}$ where k is an
integer }
8. $\theta = \tan^{-1}\left(\dfrac{b}{a}\right)$

Chapter 6 Test, Form A

(Items 1–3: 7 points each)
1. $\dfrac{\sqrt{21}}{5}$
2. left side $=$
$\dfrac{\cos x \cos y - \sin x \sin y}{\sin x \sin y} +$
$\dfrac{\sin x \sin y}{\sin x \sin y} - \dfrac{\cos x \cos y}{\sin x \sin y} =$
$\cot x \cot y$
y, x are any real numbers except $k\pi$ where k is an integer.
3. left side $= 4 \sin x \cos x +$
$2 \sin 2x \cos 2x =$
$4 \sin x \cos x +$
$2(2 \sin x \cos x)(2 \cos^2 x - 1) =$
$(4 \sin x \cos x) \cdot$
$[1 + 2 \cos^2 x - 1] =$
$4 \sin x \cos x \cdot 2 \cos^2 x =$
$8 \sin x \cos^3 x$
x is any real number.
(Items 4–8: 6 points each)
4. (c)
5. The statement is false.
Sample: Let $x = \dfrac{\pi}{2}$, then
$\cos \left(x - \dfrac{\pi}{2}\right) = \cos 0 = 1$, but
$\sin (-x) = \sin \left(-\dfrac{\pi}{2}\right) =$ -1.
6. $\dfrac{\sqrt{2 - \sqrt{2}}}{2}$

7. a.

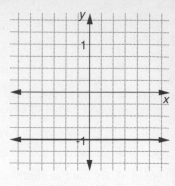

    b. $\sin 2x - (\sin x + \cos x)^2 = -1$
8. $\dfrac{56}{65}$
(Items 9–13: 8 points each)
9. $\forall$ integers k, $\dfrac{(2k + 1)\pi}{3}$,
$\dfrac{2(3k + 1)\pi}{3}$, $\dfrac{2(3k + 2)}{3}$,
$\dfrac{(6k + 5)\pi}{3}$
10. a. $x = 0$, $\dfrac{\pi}{3}$, or π
    b. $x = 0$ or $\dfrac{\pi}{3} \leq x \leq \pi$
11. $\dfrac{\sqrt{3}}{3}$
12. $\dfrac{\pi}{4}$
13. about 32.1°
(Item 14: 9 points)
14. $\theta = \sin^{-1}\left(\dfrac{h - 4}{300}\right)$ where h is
altitude of kite

Chapter 6 Test, Form B

(Items 1–3: 7 points each)
1. $-\dfrac{3}{5}$
2. left side $=$
$\dfrac{\sin x \cos y - \cos x \sin y}{\sin x \cos y} =$
$\dfrac{\sin x \cos y}{\sin x \cos y} - \dfrac{\cos x \sin y}{\sin x \cos y} =$
-cot x tan y
x is any real number except $k\pi$
where k is an integer.
y is any real number except
$\dfrac{(2k + 1)\pi}{2}$ where k is an integer.

154

3. left side =
$$\left(\frac{\cos^2 x}{\sin^2 x} + \frac{\sin^2 x}{\sin^2 x}\right) \cdot$$
$$(1 - (\cos^2 x - \sin^2 x) =$$
$$\left(\frac{\cos^2 x}{\sin^2 x} + \frac{\sin^2 x}{\sin^2 x}\right) \cdot$$
$$(1 - (\cos^2 x + \sin^2 x) =$$
$$\left(\frac{1}{\sin^2 x}\right)(2 \sin^2 x) = 2$$
x is any real number except $k\pi$ where k is an integer.

(Items 4–8:   6 points each)
4. (d)

5. Let $x = 0$. Then $\sin\left(0 + \frac{\pi}{2}\right) =$
$\sin \frac{\pi}{2} = 0$, but $-\cos (0) = 1$.

6. $\frac{\sqrt{2 - \sqrt{2}}}{2}$

7. a.

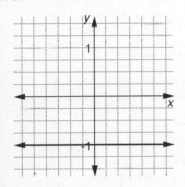

b. $\cos 2x = 2 \cos^2 x = -1$

8. $\frac{35 + \sqrt{165}}{48}$

(Items 9–13:   8 points each)

9. $x = \frac{6k + 1}{6}\pi$ or $\frac{6k + 5}{6}\pi$
(k is an integer)

10. a. $x = 0$ or $\frac{2\pi}{3}$

b. $0 \le x \le \frac{2\pi}{3}$

11. $\frac{\sqrt{2}}{2}$

12. $-\frac{\sqrt{5}}{2}$

13. about 20.8°

(Item 14:   9 points)

14. $\theta = \sin^{-1}\left(\frac{3}{\ell}\right)$

Chapter 6 Test, Cumulative Form

(Items 1–10:   6 points each)

1. No; Let $x = \frac{\pi}{4}$: left side = $\sqrt{2}$

but right side = $\frac{\sqrt{2}}{2}$.

---

2. $\frac{\sqrt{2 - \sqrt{2}}}{2}$

3. $\lim\limits_{x \to 1^+}\left(\frac{x^3}{x^4 - 1}\right) = \infty$

4. $\cos(\pi + x) =$
$\cos \pi \cos x - \sin \pi \sin x =$
$(-1)\cos x - (0)\sin x = -\cos x$

5. $\frac{1760m}{400 + m^2}$

6. $f(x) = \frac{1}{(x + 3)(x - 5)}$

7. $\sqrt{3}$

8. a. $x = k\pi$ or $\frac{\pi}{6} + 2k\pi$ or
$\frac{5\pi}{6} + 2k\pi$ (k is an integer)

b. $\frac{\pi}{6} < x < \frac{5\pi}{6}$ or $\pi < x < 2\pi$

9. 110000_2

10. $\frac{11}{3}$

(Item 11:   8 points)
11. Any perfect square is of the form n^2 where n is an integer. By the Quotient-Remainder Theorem, n can be written in the form $n = 3k + r$ where $r = 0, 1,$ or 2. Thus either $n = 3k$, $n = 3k + 1$, or $n = 3k + 2$. If $n = 3k$, then $n^2 = 9k^2$ which is a multiple of 3. If $n = 3k + 1$, then $n^2 = 9k^2 + 6k + 1 = 3(3k^2 + 2k) + 1$ which is 1 more than a multiple of 3. If $n = 3k + 2$, then $n^2 = 9k^2 + 12k + 4 = 3(3k^2 + 4k + 1) + 1$ which is 1 more than a multiple of 3.
(Item 12:   8 points)
12. $t < .2$ or $t > 4.5$

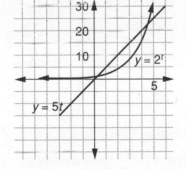

(Item 13:   10 points)
13. left side =
$$\frac{1 + \frac{\sin x}{\cos x}}{1 + \frac{\cos x}{\sin x}} =$$
$$\frac{\cos x \sin x + \sin^2 x}{\cos x \sin x + \cos^2 x} =$$
$$\frac{\sin x (\cos x + \sin x)}{\cos x (\sin x + \cos x)} =$$
$$\frac{\sin x}{\cos x} = \tan x$$

---

domain: {all real numbers except $\frac{k\pi}{2}$ and $\frac{3\pi}{4} + k\pi$ where k is an integer}
(Items 14–15:   7 points each)

14. $(f \cdot g)(x) = \frac{5}{x + 3}$

15. a. $\theta = \sin^{-1}\left(\frac{d}{15}\right)$

b. $d = 8 \sin \phi$

c. $\theta = \sin^{-1}\left(\frac{8 \sin \phi}{15}\right)$

Comprehensive Test, Chapters 1–6

(Items 1–25:   4 points each)
1. (c)
2. (d)
3. (d)
4. (d)
5. (b)
6. (b)
7. (b)
8. (d)
9. (a)
10. (d)
11. (b)
12. (d)
13. (a)
14. (c)
15. (b)
16. (d)
17. (d)
18. (b)
19. (d)
20. (c)
21. (a)
22. (d)
23. (c)
24. (c)
25. (c)

Quiz for Lessons 7-1 through 7-3

1. a. 1, 3, 7, 15, 31
b. $a_n = 2^n - 1$
2. a. 1296
b. 1296
3. a. $t_j = 8 + 5(j + 1)$
b. explicit

4. $\sum\limits_{i=3}^{k}(i^2 + 2) + [(k + 1)^2 + 2]$

5. $a_1 = 3^{1-1} + 1 = 2 = b_1$
$a_{k+1} = 3^{k+1-1} + 1 =$
$3^{1+k-1} + 3 - 3 + 1 =$
$3(3^{k-1} + 1) - 2 = 3a_k - 2$
Thus, the formula $a_n = 3^{n-1} + 1$ satisfies the recursive definition of b.
6. a. n
b. $\begin{cases} c_1 = 0 \\ c_{k+1} = c_k + k \text{ for } k \ge 1 \end{cases}$

c.

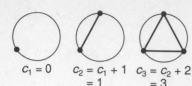

$c_1 = 0 \qquad c_2 = c_1 + 1 \qquad c_3 = c_2 + 2$
$\qquad\qquad\quad = 1 \qquad\qquad = 3$

Quiz for Lessons 7-4 through 7-6

1. a. $\displaystyle\sum_{j=1}^{20} 4(.75)^j$

b. 11.95

2. Suppose that $S(n)$ is a statement in n, where n is a positive integer. To prove that $S(n)$ is true $\forall\ n \geq 1$, prove:
(1) $S(1)$ is true, and
(2) $S(k)$ is true for an integer $k \Rightarrow S(k + 1)$ is true.

3. a. proving that 8 is a factor of $3^{2(1)} - 1$

b. assuming that 8 is a factor of $3^{2k} - 1$ for an integer k.

c. that 8 is a factor of $3^{2(k+1)} - 1$

4. Let $S(n)$ be:
$$\frac{1}{2} + \frac{1}{2^2} + \dots + \frac{1}{2^n} = 1 - \frac{1}{2^n}.$$

(1) Prove $S(1)$ is true:
$\frac{1}{2} = 1 - \frac{1}{2}$, which is true.

(2) Assume $S(k)$ is true for an integer k:
$$\frac{1}{2} + \frac{1}{2^2} + \dots + \frac{1}{2^k} = 1 - \frac{1}{2^k}.$$

Prove $S(k + 1)$ is true:
$$\frac{1}{2} + \frac{1}{2^2} + \dots + \frac{1}{2^k} + \frac{1}{2^{k+1}} =$$
$$1 - \frac{1}{2^k} + \frac{1}{2^{k+1}} =$$
$$1 - \frac{2}{2} \cdot \frac{1}{2^k} + \frac{1}{2^{k+1}} =$$
$$1 - \frac{2}{2^{k+1}} + \frac{1}{2^{k+1}} = 1 - \frac{1}{2^{k+1}},$$

so $S(k + 1)$ is true.
∴ By induction, $S(n)$ is true $\forall$ integer $n \geq 1$.

Chapter 7 Test, Form A

(Items 1–9: 7 points each)
1. 3, 5, 9, 17, 33
2. $a_n = 2^n + 1$
3. $C_1 = 4$
$C_{k+1} = C_k \cdot 4,\ k \geq 1$
4. False

5. $\displaystyle\sum_{j=1}^{6} j(j + 1)$

6. $\displaystyle\sum_{j=2}^{k} j(j + 2) + [(k + 1)(k + 2)]$

---

7. a. 2.4992

b. Yes, $\frac{5}{2}$

8. The inductive assumptions are different. In the former, $S(k)$ is assumed true for a positive integer k. In the latter, $S(1)$, $S(2)$, $S(3)$, ... , $S(k)$ are all assumed true.

9. $b_1 = 3^1 - 1 = 2 = a_1$
$b_{k+1} = 3^{k+1} - 1 =$
$3^{k+1} - 3 + 3 - 1 =$
$3(3^k - 1) + 2 =$
$3(b_k) + 2$
Thus b satisfies the recursive formula for a.

(Item 10: 13 points)
10. Let $S(n)$: 3 is a factor of $n^3 + 5n$. Show that $S(1)$ is true: 3 is a factor of $1^3 + 5(1) = 6$. Assume that $S(k)$ is true. Show that $S(k + 1)$ is true.
$(k + 1)^3 + 5(k + 1) =$
$(k^3 + 5k) + 3(k^2 + k + 2)$
Since 3 is a factor of $k^3 + 5k$,
$k^3 + 5k = 3m$ for some integer m.
$(k + 1)^3 + 5(k + 1) =$
$3m + 3(k^2 + k + 2) =$
$3(m + k^2 + k + 2)$, a multiple of 3. So $S(k + 1)$ is true. By induction, $S(n)$ is true for all positive integers n.

(Items 11–12: 6 points each)
11. a. showing that a_1, a_2, and a_3 are odd
b. assuming that a_1, a_2, a_3, ... , a_k are odd for every integer from 3 to k
c. that a_{k+1} is odd

12. $\frac{3}{2}$

(Item 13: 12 points)
13.

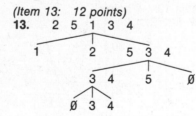

2 5 1 3 4

1 2 5 3 4

3 4 5 Ø

Ø 3 4

1 2 3 4 5

Chapter 7 Test, Form B

(Items 1–9: 7 points each)
1. 0, 3, 8, 15, 24
2. $a_n = n^2 - 1$
3. $\begin{cases} R_1 = 5 \\ R_{k+1} = 5 \cdot R_k \text{ for all } k \geq 1 \end{cases}$
4. True

5. $\displaystyle\sum_{j=0}^{6} \frac{j}{j + 1}$

6. $\displaystyle\sum_{i=0}^{n} (i^2 + 1) + [(n + 1)^2 + 1]$

---

7. a. 3.996

b. Yes, 4

8. In the former, the basis step may have to establish the truth of $S(a)$, $S(a + 1)$, $S(a + 2)$, ... , $S(a + b)$, but in the latter, only $S(a)$ must be shown true (where a and b are integers).

9. $b_1 = 3 \cdot 2^{1-1} - 1 = 2 = a_1$
$b_{k+1} = 3 \cdot 2^{k+1-1} - 1 =$
$3 \cdot 2 \cdot 2^{k-1} - 2 + 2 - 1 =$
$2(3 \cdot 2^{k-1} - 1) + 1 =$
$2b_k + 1$,
so b satisfies the recursive definition of a.

(Item 10: 13 points)
10. Let $S(n)$: 6 is a factor of $2n^3 + 4n$.
Show that $S(1)$ is true: 6 is a factor of $2(1)^3 + 4(1) = 6$. Assume that $S(k)$ is true. Show that $S(k + 1)$ is true.
$2(k + 1)^3 + 4(k + 1) =$
$(2k^3 + 4k) + 6(k^2 + k + 1)$
Since 6 is a factor of $2k^3 + 4k$, $2k^3 + 4k = 6m$ for some integer m.
$2(k + 1)^3 + 4(k + 1) =$
$6m + 6(k^2 + k + 1) =$
$6(m + k^2 + k + 1)$, a multiple of 6. So $S(k + 1)$ is true. By induction, $S(n)$ is true for all positive integers n.

(Item 11–12: 6 points each)
11. a. the proof that a_1, a_2, and a_3 are all odd
b. the assumption that a_1, a_2, a_3, ... , a_k are odd for all integers from 3 to k
c. that a_{k+1} is odd

12. 3

(Item 13: 12 points)

13.

8	9	9
6	8	8
2 →	6 →	6
9	2	5
5	5	2
	↑	↑
	after	after
	pass	pass
	1	2

sorted

Chapter 7 Test, Cumulative Form

(Items 1–13: 7 points each)
1. $r_1 = 2$
$r_{k+1} = 2r_k$ for $k \geq 1$

2. $\theta = \tan^{-1}\left(\dfrac{42}{d}\right)$

3. $\displaystyle\sum_{j=3}^{9} j^{j+1}$

156

4. $0 \leq x < \frac{\pi}{2}$, or

$\frac{3\pi}{4} < x < \frac{3\pi}{2}$, or

$\frac{7\pi}{4} < x < 2\pi$

5. $\frac{3\pi}{4}$

6. $\sqrt{2}$ and $\sqrt{2}$;
$\sqrt{2}\sqrt{2} = \sqrt{4} = 2$,
a rational number

7. a. 2, 5, 10, 17, 26
b. $a_n = n^2 + 1$
c. $a_1 = 1^2 + 1 = 2$
$a_{k+1} = (k + 1)^2 + 1 =$
$k^2 + 2k + 1 + 1 =$
$(k^2 + 1) + 2k + 1 =$
$a_k + 2k + 1$,
so the explicit formula generates a sequence which satisfies the recursive formula.

8. 12
9. a. .77777

b. Yes, $\frac{7}{9}$

10. 3 1 5 2 9
   1 3 2 5 9
   1 2 3 5 9
11. a.

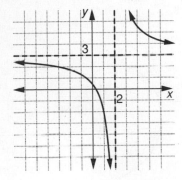

b. $\lim_{x \to -\infty} f(x) = \lim_{x \to \infty} f(x) = 3$
c. $x = 2$
12. left side =
$\sin^2 x + 2 \sin x \cos x + \cos^2 x$
$= 1 + 2 \sin x \cos x = 1 \sin 2x$
domain = {all real numbers}
13. a. proving that c_1 and c_2 are
multiples of 5
b. assuming that c_1, c_2,
c_3, ... , c_k are multiples of 5
for every integer from 2 to k
c. that c_{k+1} is a multiple of 5

(Item 14: 9 points)
14. Let $S(n)$:

$$\sum_{i=1}^{n} \frac{1}{(2i - 1)(2i + 1)} = \frac{n}{2n + 1}.$$

Show that $S(1)$ is true:

$$\sum_{i=1}^{1} \frac{1}{(2i - 1)(2i + 1)} =$$

$$\frac{1}{(2(1) - 1)(2(1) + 1)} = \frac{1}{3} =$$

$$\frac{1}{2(1) + 1}.$$

Assume that $S(k)$ is true.
Show that $S(k + 1)$ is true.

$$\sum_{i=1}^{k+1} \frac{1}{(2i - 1)(2i + 1)} =$$

$$\sum_{i=1}^{k} \frac{1}{(2i - 1)(2i + 1)} =$$

$$\frac{1}{(2(k + 1) - 1)(2(k + 1) + 1)} =$$

$$\frac{k}{2k + 1} + \frac{1}{(2k + 1)(2k + 3)} =$$

$$\frac{(2k + 1)(k + 1)}{(2k + 1)(2k + 3)} =$$

$$\frac{k + 1}{2k + 3} = \frac{k + 1}{2(k + 1) + 1}$$

So $S(k + 1)$ is true. So $S(n)$ is
true for all positive integers n.

Quiz for Lessons 8-1 through 8-3

1. $5 + 12i$; [13, 67.38°];
13(cos 67.38° + i sin 67.38°)
2. $-2.83 + 2.83i$;
$(-2.83, 2.83)$; $\left[4, \frac{3\pi}{4}\right]$
3. $z \cdot w =$
4(cos 105° + i sin 105°)
$\frac{z}{w} = \cos 195° + i \sin 195°$
4. $z + w = (3, -3)$
$z \cdot w = (-12, -1)$
5.

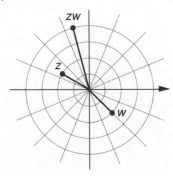

$[12.04, -175°] = (-12, -1)$
6. $\frac{30}{13} - \frac{20}{13}i$ amps

7. Let $z = a + bi$ where a, b are
real (a and b nonzero).
Then

$$\frac{1}{z} = \frac{1}{a + bi} \cdot \frac{a - bi}{a - bi} = \frac{a - bi}{a^2 + b^2}$$

$$= \frac{\bar{z}}{|z|^2}$$

Quiz for Lessons 8-4 through 8-7

1.

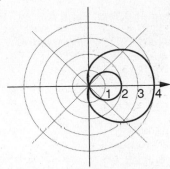

limaçon
2.

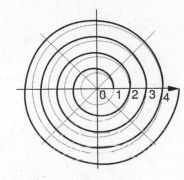

spiral of Archimedes
3. 128(cos 140° + i sin 140°)
4. [2, 10°], [2, 70°], [2, 130°],
[2, 190°], [2, 250°], [2, 310°]

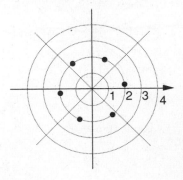

5. a. 1
b. 2
c. 1
d. 0

6. By De Moivre's Theorem

$$\frac{z^n}{z^m} = \frac{[r, \theta]^n}{[r, \theta]^m} = \frac{[r^n, n\theta]}{[r^m, m\theta]} =$$

$$[r^n, n\theta] \cdot \frac{1}{[r^m, m\theta]} =$$

$$[r^n, n\theta] \cdot [r^{-m}, -m\theta]$$

By the Geometric Multiplication Theorem,

$$\frac{z^n}{z^m} = [r^n \cdot r^{-m}, n\theta + (-m\theta)] =$$

$$[r^{n-m}, (n - m)\theta] = z^{n-m}$$

Chapter 8 Test, Form A

(Items 1–5: 7 points each)
1. a. $-3 + 4i$, $[5, 127°]$
 b. -3, $[3, \pi]$
2. a. $2 + 3\sqrt{3}i$

 b. $2 - \frac{2}{3}\sqrt{3}i$

3. $[3, 45°]$
4. 20 volts
5. $[800\sqrt{5}, 0°]$
(Items 6–10: 9 points each)
6. $-6, 3 + 3\sqrt{3}i, 3 - 3\sqrt{3}i$

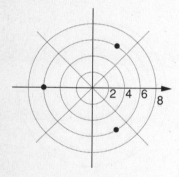

7.

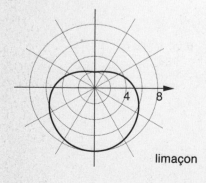

twelve-leafed rose
8.

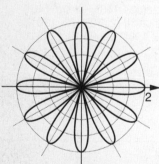

limaçon

---

9. $2i$(mult. 1), $-2i$(mult. 1), 2(mult. 2)
10.

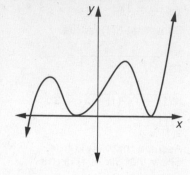

(Items 11–14: 5 points each)
11. 5
12. Let $z = a + bi$ where a and b are real. Then $\bar{z} = a - bi$.
$z - \bar{z} = a + bi - (a - bi) =$
$a - a + bi + bi = 2bi$
$2bi$ is always an imaginary number. $z - \bar{z}$ is an imaginary number.

13. $3 + 2i + (-1 + 2i) = 2 + 4i$

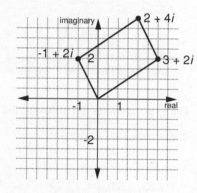

14. $[4, 225°]$

Chapter 8 Test, Form B

(Items 1–5: 7 points each)
1. a. $-4i$, $\left[4, \frac{3\pi}{2} \right]$

 b. $\frac{3}{2} + \frac{\sqrt{3}}{2}i$, $\left[3, \frac{\pi}{3} \right]$

2. a. $18 + 5\sqrt{3}\,i$
 b. $5 + 5\sqrt{3}\,i$

3. $\left[\frac{2}{5}, 105° \right]$

4. $\frac{15}{16} - \frac{15\sqrt{3}}{16}i$

5. $\left[512, \frac{\pi}{4} \right]$

(Items 6–10: 9 points each)
6.

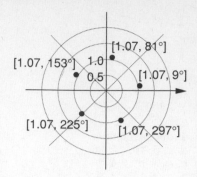

[1.07, 81°]
[1.07, 153°] 1.0
0.5
[1.07, 9°]
[1.07, 225°]
[1.07, 297°]

7.

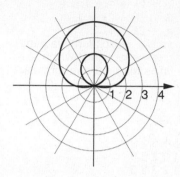

limaçon
8.

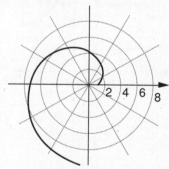

spiral of Archimedes
9. $\pm\frac{3}{2}i, -\frac{3}{2}, 1$

Each has multiplicity 1.
10.

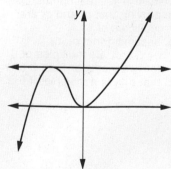

(Items 11–14: 5 points each)
11. 7
12. Let $z = a + bi$ where a and b are real. Then $\bar{z} = a - bi$. So $z\bar{z} = (a + bi)(a - bi) = a^2 + b^2 + (ab - ba)i = a^2 + b^2$, which is a real number.

13.
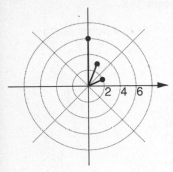

14. [5, 315°]

Chapter 8 Test, Cumulative Form

(Items 1–4: 7 points each)
1. $5 + 4i$
2.
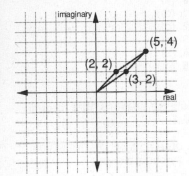

3. a. $\sum_{j=0}^{\infty} \left(\frac{1}{3}\right)^j$

b. $\frac{3}{2}$

4. $\frac{6}{5} + \frac{8}{5}i$ amps

(Items 5–6: 8 points each)
5.
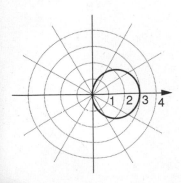

circle

6.
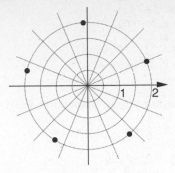

Either location of x-axis is acceptable.

(Items 7–8: 7 points each)
7. $\left[3.8, \frac{4\pi}{3}\right]$

8. $(x - 2)(x + 3)(x + 2i)(x - 2i) = x^4 + x^3 - 2x^2 + 4x - 24$

(Item 9: 12 points)
9. Use the Principle of Mathematical Induction to prove that $n^3 + 2n$ is divisible by 3 for all positive integers. Let $S(n): n^3 + 2n$ is divisible by 3.
(1) Basis step: Show that $S(1)$ is true: $1^3 + 2 \cdot 1$ is divisible by 3. Since the above expression is 3, and $3 \div 3 = 1$, $S(1)$ is clearly true.
(2) Inductive step: Show that $S(k)$ implies $S(k + 1)$ for all integers $k \geq 1$.
Assume that $S(k)$ is true for some particular but arbitrarily chosen integer k. That is, assume $S(k): k^3 + 2k$ is divisible by 3. Show $S(k + 1)$ is true:
$(k + 1)^3 + 2(k + 1) =$
$k^3 + 3k^2 + 5k + 3 =$
$(k^3 + 2k) + 3k^2 + 3k + 3.$
By the inductive assumption, $k^3 + 2k$ is divisible by 3. Also, all of the remaining terms have coefficient 3 and so are divisible by 3. By the Factor of a Sum Theorem, $(k^3 + 2k) + 3k^2 + 3k + 3$ is divisible by 3 and $S(k + 1)$ is true. From 1 and 2 using the principle of Mathematical Induction, $n^3 + 2n$ is divisible by 3 for all positive integers n.
(Items 10–14: 6 points each)
10. 3, 2, 17, 46, 81

11.
$L = 5, 1, 10, 12, 3, 2, 11$
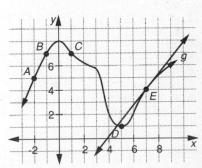

	First Pass:	1 3 2 5 10 12 11
	Second Pass:	1 3 2 5 10 12 11
	Third Pass:	1 2 3 5 10 11 12

12. a. $\lim_{x \to -\infty} f(x) = 1$; $\lim_{x \to \infty} f(x) = 1$
b. $x = -3$ essential and $x = -2$ removable
c. $x = -3$
  $y = 1$
13. $3 \cdot 3 \cdot 3 \cdot 11 \cdot 13 = 3^3 \cdot 11 \cdot 13$
14. a. 110011_2
b. 51

Quiz for Lessons 9-1 through 9-3

1. a. about 12814 $\frac{\text{lawyers}}{\text{year}}$

b. 22598 $\frac{\text{lawyers}}{\text{year}}$

c. The rate of change in the number of lawyers has almost doubled.

2. $f'(x) = \lim_{h \to 0} \frac{f(x + h) - f(x)}{h}$

3. $f'(x) = 7$
4. a. 2

b. $-\frac{3}{2}$

c.

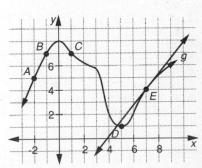

d. negative

5. a. $70 - 32t - 16\Delta t$
b. -74 ft/sec
c. $h'(t) = 70 - 32t$
d. -58 ft/sec

Chapter 9 Test, Form A

(Items 1–10: 9 points each)

1. a. 160 $\dfrac{\text{millions of dollars}}{\text{year}}$

b. 34 $\dfrac{\text{millions of dollars}}{\text{year}}$

c. The rate of spending by NASA has increased.

2. a. -1
b. (b)
c. (b)
d. -5

3. a. $30 + 5\Delta x$
b. 31.25

4. (e)

5. -1

6. (c)

7. positive

8. a. -16 ft/sec
b. -32 ft/sec²

9. a. 76 ft
b. 0 m/sec

10. a. $x > 0$
b. $x < 0$

(Item 11: 10 points)
11. a., b. See below.

Chapter 9 Test, Form B

(Items 1–10: 9 points each)
1. a. about 32 students fewer per year
b. about 78 students more per year
c. The number of students has increased an average of 78 students per year from 1981 to 1983. In the period 1973–1980, the number of students has decreased.

2. a. $-\dfrac{3}{5}$

b. (d)
c. (d)
d. -1.5

3. a. $12 + 3\Delta x$
b. 13.5

4. (d)

5. -1

6. (c)

7. negative

8. a. 19.6 m/sec
b. -9.8 m/sec²

---

9. a. 143.5 m
b. 0 m/sec

10. a. $x < 5$
b. $x > 5$

(Item 11: 10 points)
11. a. See below.

Chapter 9 Test, Cumulative Form

(Items 1–10: 10 points each)
1. (a)

2. a. $(-2, -2\sqrt{3})$

b. $\left(\dfrac{-5\sqrt{2}}{2}, \dfrac{5\sqrt{2}}{2}\right)$

3. a. $-\dfrac{1}{3}$

b. (c)
c. 0
d. $-7 < x < -3$ and $-1 < x < 5$

4. a. removable
b. $\lim\limits_{x\to\infty} h(x) = \lim\limits_{x\to-\infty} h(x) = 0$

c. $\dfrac{1}{3}$

5. a. $2x + 6 + \Delta x$
b. 0

6. a. 7
b. $p(x) = x^2(x - (2 + i)) \cdot (x - (2 - i))(x - i)(x + i) \cdot (x - 3)$

7. a. $f'(x) = 12x - 2$

b. $x < -\dfrac{2}{3}$ and $x > 1$

c. 2.481 at $x = -\dfrac{2}{3}$ and 2 at $x = 1$

8. a. 2
b. $\sqrt[3]{2}, -1 - \sqrt{3}i$
c.

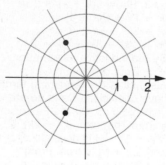

11. a. $f'(x) = \lim\limits_{h\to0} \dfrac{-6(x + h)^2 + 10 - (-6x^2 + 10)}{h} = -12x$

---

9. a. $h'(t) = 250 - 32t$
b. 58 ft/sec
c. -32 ft/sec²
d. about 977 ft

10. $x = 25$

Comprehensive Test, Chapters 1–9

(Items 1–25: 4 points each)
1. (a)
2. (d)
3. (b)
4. (c)
5. (c)
6. (c)
7. (a)
8. (b)
9. (d)
10. (b)
11. (d)
12. (c)
13. (a)
14. (b)
15. (b)
16. (d)
17. (a)
18. (c)
19. (c)
20. (a)
21. (d)
22. (d)
23. (a)
24. (b)
25. (c)

Quiz for Lessons 10-1 through 10-3

1. ordered symbols, repetition of symbols allowed

2.

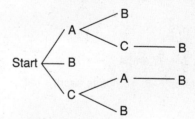

---

11. a. $g'(x) = \lim\limits_{h\to0} \dfrac{-7(x + h)^2 + 5 - (-7x^2 + 5)}{h} = \lim\limits_{h\to0} (-14x - 7h) = -14x$
b. By the theorem, $g'(x) = (2)(-7x) = -14x$.

3. Although in each case two choices are being made from a group of 5, and 2 from a group of 8, in B order it is important, whereas in A it is not. For example, the prom king and runner-up could be reversed, resulting in a different selection.

4. 11!, or 39,916,800

5. 7

6. 5040

7. a. $P(9, 4) = \dfrac{9!}{5!}$,

$P(9 - 4, 2) = \dfrac{5!}{3!}$,

$P(9, 6) = \dfrac{9!}{3!}$,

so $P(9, 4) \cdot P(9 - 4, 2) =$

$\dfrac{9!}{5!} \cdot \dfrac{5!}{3!} = \dfrac{9!}{3!} = P(9, 6)$.

b. $P(n, r) \cdot P(n - r, s) =$

$\dfrac{n!}{(n - r)!} \cdot \dfrac{(n - r)!}{(n - r - s)!} =$

$\dfrac{n!}{[n - (r + s)]!} = P(n, r + s)$

Quiz for Lessons 10-4 through 10-6

1. P
2. C
3. C
4. P
5. 75,287,520
6. .994

7. $\dbinom{10}{3}$

8. $5,852,925a^{22}b^8$

Chapter 10 Test, Form A

(Items 1–12: 5 points each)
1. ordered symbols without repetition
2. unordered symbols without repetition
3. See below.
4. 8375
5. 3,603,600
6. 792

7. $C(n, 1) = \dfrac{n!}{1!(n - 1)!} =$

$\dfrac{n \cdot (n - 1)(n - 2) \cdot \ldots \cdot 1}{1 \cdot (n - 1)(n - 2) \cdot \ldots \cdot 1} = n$

8. 20
9. 125,000
10. 117,600
11. 70,560
12. 462

(Items 13–17: 8 points each)
13. a. 1 7 21 35 35 21 7 1
b. $x^7 + 7x^6y + 21x^5y^2 + 35x^4y^3 + 35x^3y^4 + 21x^2y^5 + 7xy^6 + y^7$

14. $17010x^6y^4$

15. $b = n - a$; $\dbinom{n}{a} = \dfrac{n!}{a!(n - a)!}$;

$\dbinom{n}{b} = \dfrac{n!}{(n - a)!(n - (n - a))!} =$

$\dfrac{n!}{(n - a)!a!} = \dfrac{n!}{a!(n - a)!} = \dbinom{n}{a}$

16. $\dbinom{6}{0} + \dbinom{6}{1} + \dbinom{6}{2} + \dbinom{6}{3} +$

$\dbinom{6}{4} + \dbinom{6}{5} + \dbinom{6}{6}$

17. $\approx .058$

Chapter 10 Test, Form B

(Items 1–12: 5 points each)
1. ordered symbols with repetition
2. ordered symbols without repetition
3. See below.
4. 500
5. 165
6. 11880

7. $P(n, n) = \dfrac{n!}{(n - n)!} = \dfrac{n!}{0!} =$

$\dfrac{n!}{1} = n!$

8. 35
9. 544,320
10. 10,000
11. 4,251,528
12. 1140

(Items 13–17: 8 points each)
13. a. 1 6 15 20 15 6 1
b. $x^6 - 6x^5y + 15x^4y^2 - 20x^3y^3 + 15x^2y^4 - 6xy^5 + y^6$

14. $5376x^6y^3$

3.

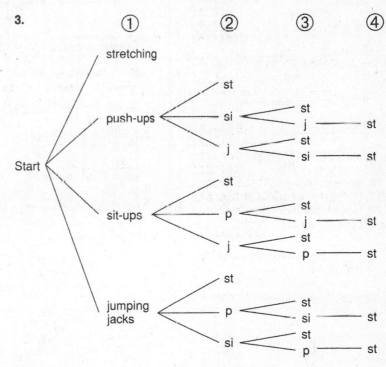

3.

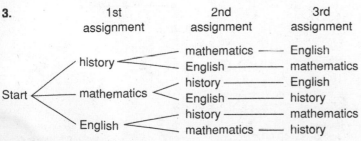

15. $\binom{n}{a} = \dfrac{n!}{a!(n-a)!}$ If $a + b = n$, then $a = n - b$. So $\binom{n}{a} =$

$\dfrac{n!}{(n-b)!(n-(n-b)!)} =$

$\dfrac{n!}{(n-b)!b!} = \binom{n}{b}$

16. $\binom{7}{1} + \binom{7}{2} + \binom{7}{3} + \binom{7}{4} +$

$\binom{7}{5} + \binom{7}{6} + \binom{7}{7}$

17. $\approx .023$

Chapter 10 Test, Cumulative Form

(Items 1–12: 5 points each)

1. $\binom{9}{6} = 84$

2. $\binom{11}{8} = 165$

3. 625
4. $6x + 4$
5. 2970
6. 32
7. a. No
   b. Yes

8. $P(7, 3) = \dfrac{7!}{(7-3)!} =$

$\dfrac{7 \cdot 6 \cdot 5 \cdot 4 \cdot 3 \cdot 2 \cdot 1}{4 \cdot 3 \cdot 2 \cdot 1} =$

$7 \cdot 6 \cdot 5 = 210;$

$3!C(7, 3) = \dfrac{3!}{1} \cdot \dfrac{7!}{3!(7-3)!} =$

$\dfrac{7 \cdot 6 \cdot 5 \cdot 4 \cdot 3 \cdot 2 \cdot 1}{4 \cdot 3 \cdot 2 \cdot 1} = 210$

so $P(7, 3) = 3!C(7, 3)$.

9. $5 \cdot 3! \cdot 4! = 720$
10. 4
11. $(x - 2)^5$
12. See below.

12.

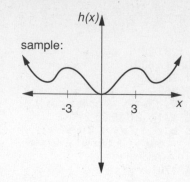

	1st	2nd	3rd

Start — javelin — shotput — 100 m
Start — javelin — 100 m — shotput
Start — shotput — javelin — 100 m
Start — shotput — 100 m — javelin
Start — 100 m dash — javelin — shotput
Start — 100 m dash — shotput — javelin

(Items 13–17: 8 points each)
13. sample:

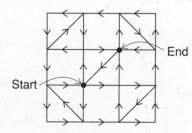

sample: $h(x)$

14. True
15. $2\sqrt{5} + \sqrt{15}$
16. 36.25 feet
17. $\dfrac{-2\sqrt{10} - 2}{9}$

Quiz for Lessons 11-1 through 11-4

1. a.

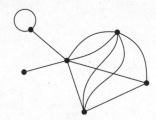

Start   End

b. No. Two vertices have odd degree.

2. $\begin{bmatrix} 0 & 0 & 0 & 1 \\ 1 & 2 & 1 & 1 \\ 2 & 0 & 1 & 1 \\ 0 & 0 & 0 & 0 \end{bmatrix}$

3. (b), (d)
4.

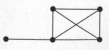

---

5. No. If it were possible, then the 17 vertices would each have degree 3. Then the total degree would be $3 \times 17 = 51$, an odd number.

6. a.

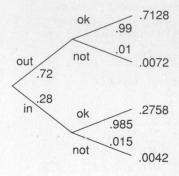

b. .6315

Chapter 11 Test, Form A

(Items 1–12: 7 points each)
1. Yes. *PDBECAP*
2.

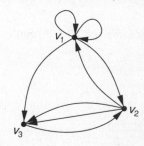

3. a. e_6 or e_9
   b. e_5
4.

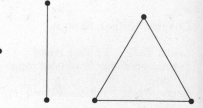

5. No. $\deg(v_i) = 5$ for each v_i
6. $x = 1, y = 3$
7. 6
8.

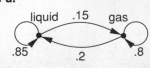

9. a.

liquid .15 gas
.85   .2   .8

b. $\dfrac{4}{7}$

---

10. a. v_2, v_3, v_4
  b. $e_3, 3_6$
  c. e_3 and e_7 or e_6 and e_7
11. a. Yes
  b. All vertices have even degree.
12. a. Yes

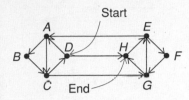

  b. No. Not all vertices have even degree.
(Item 13: 16 points)
13. a.

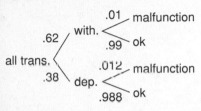

  b. about 42%

Chapter 11 Test, Form B

(Items 1–12: 7 points each)
1. Yes. home - grocery - gas station - post office - airport - bank - home
2.

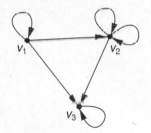

3. a. e_1 or e_2
  b. e_3 or e_7
4.

5. Yes. $\deg(v_i) = $ even $\forall\ v_1$
6. $x = 2, y = 0$
7. 108
8. $\sum \deg(v_i) = $ odd $\therefore$ no such graph
9. a.

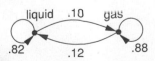

  b. $\dfrac{3}{5}$

10. a. v_1, v_2, v_3, v_5
  b. e_6 and e_7
  c. e_6 and e_8 or e_7 and e_8
11. a. No
  b.

12. a. Yes

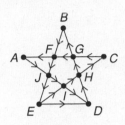

  Start at E.
  End at D.
  b. No. Not all vertices have even degree.
(Item 13: 16 points)
13. a. See below.
  b. $\approx .0063$

Chapter 11 Test, Cumulative Form

(Items 1–11: 7 points each)
1. Yes. $\deg(v_i) = $ even v_i

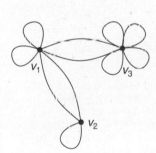

2. 4950
3. $\dfrac{\sqrt{3}}{2}$
4.

13. a.

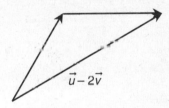

5. same probability
6. 21
7. 3
8. 9
9. 362,880
10. 14
11. $f(g(x)) = f\left(\dfrac{x}{2} + \dfrac{5}{2}\right) =$

  $2\left(\dfrac{x}{2} + \dfrac{5}{2}\right) - 5 = x;$

  $g(f(x)) = g(2x - 5) =$
  $\dfrac{2x - 5}{2} + \dfrac{5}{2} = x - \dfrac{5}{2} + \dfrac{5}{2} = x,$

  so $f(g(x)) = g(f(x)) = x.$
(Item 12: 8 points)
12. a.

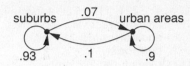

  b. $\dfrac{10}{17}$

(Items 13–15: 5 points each)
13. 36
14. Yes. Both have 6 vertices and 9 edges, with 3 edges per vertex.
15. $q(x) = x^3 - x^2 + 4x + 3$
  $r(x) = 9$

Quiz for Lessons 12-1 through 12-3

1. $\vec{u} + \vec{v} = (6, -7) + (3, 4) =$
  $(9, -3) = -3(-3, 1) = -3\vec{w}$
2.

3. a. (-8, 3)
b.

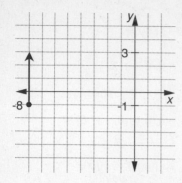

4. $(x - 2, y + 5) = t(3, -2)$
5. a. $\approx$ (-221, 117); The airplane is moving westward 221 miles and northward 117 miles each hour.
  b. magnitude: 228 mph; direction: 146°

Quiz for Lessons 12-4 through 12-6

1. 24
2. 1 or -6
3. center: (1, -3, 2)
  radius: 7
4. $\vec{u} \cdot \vec{v} = xky + (-ykx) = 0$ so $\vec{u}$ and $\vec{v}$ are orthogonal.
5. a., c.

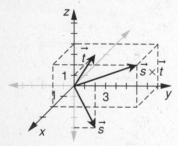

  b. (2, 8, 4)
  d. $\approx$ 114°

Chapter 12 Test, Form A

(Items 1–10: 7 points each)
1. $\sqrt{29}$
2. 1
3. 102°
4. perpendicular
5. (1, 10, 5)
6. (30, -4, 2)
7. Let $\vec{u} = (x, y, z)$ and $\vec{v} = k\vec{u}$.
  Then $\vec{v} = (kx, ky, kz)$.
  $\vec{u} \cdot \vec{v} =$
  $(x, y, z) \cdot (kx, ky, kz) =$
  $(kx^2, ky^2, kz^2) =$
  $k(x^2, y^2, z^2) = k|\vec{u}|^2$

---

8. a., d.

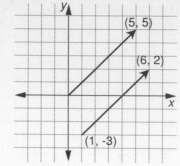

b. (5, 5)
c. $[5\sqrt{2}, 45°]$
9. a.

b.

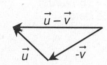

10.

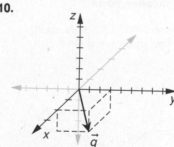

(Items 11–15: 6 points each)
11. $(x - 4)^2 + (y - 2)^2 + (z + 1)^2 = 16$
12. $-2(y + 1) + 5(z + 3) = 0$
13. $x = 4 - 3t, y = -1 + 3t$
14. (-6.4, 7.7)
15. 2.8 knots, 0° east

Chapter 12 Test, Form B

(Items 1–10: 7 points each)
1. $\sqrt{10}$
2. -17
3. 162°
4. neither
5. (1, -1, -8)
6. (-11, 5, -2)
7. Let $\vec{u} = (x, y)$. Since $\vec{u} + \vec{v} = 0$, $\vec{v} = -\vec{u} =$ (-x, -y). So $\vec{u} \cdot \vec{v} =$
  $(x, y) \cdot (-x, -y) =$
  $(-x^2) + (-y^2) =$
  $-(x^2 + y^2) = -|\vec{u}|^2$

---

8. a., d.

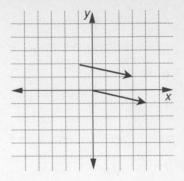

b. (4, -1)
c. $[\sqrt{17}, 346°]$
9. a.

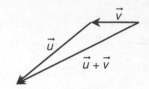

b.

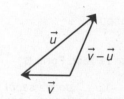

10.

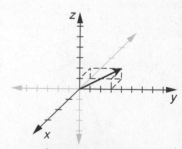

(Items 11–15: 6 points each)
11. $(x + 3)^2 + (y - 2)^2 + (z + 1)^2 = 25^2$
12. $8(x + 2) = 6(y - 0) + 3(z - 5) = 0$
13. $x = -3 - 4t, y = -5 + 2t$
14. about (-12, 33)
15. 24.8 mph, 77° west of north

Chapter 12 Test, Cumulative Form

(Items 1–10: 7 points each)
1. 6
2. 10
3. $(x + 3, y - 2) = t(-1, -4)$

164

4.

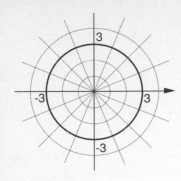

5. $(x - 4)^2 + (y + 2)^2 + z^2 = 6^2$
6. No
7. 143°
8. 45
9. a. magnitude: $\sqrt{89}$
     direction: 328°
b.

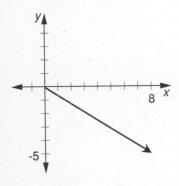

10. $\begin{bmatrix} 1 & 1 & 1 & 0 \\ 1 & 0 & 0 & 0 \\ 0 & 1 & 1 & 0 \\ 0 & 2 & 1 & 0 \end{bmatrix}$

(Items 11–16: 5 points each)
11. 529 mph; 42° north of west
12. (b)
13. Neither, because $\nexists\ k$ such
     that $\vec{u} = k\vec{v}$, and $\vec{u} \cdot \vec{v} \neq 0$.
14. No. The total degree in the
     handshake graph has to be
     even, but 23×3 is odd.
15. $y - 3(z + 2) = 0$
16. $y = -2 \sin\left(\frac{1}{2}x\right)$

Quiz for Lessons 13-1 through 13-4

1.

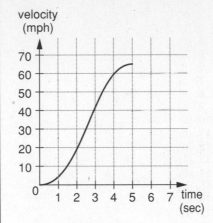

left endpoints:
$\approx .0347$ miles ≈ 183 feet
right endpoints:
$\approx .0528$ miles ≈ 279 feet
2. 9
3. $\int_0^2 (\sqrt{9 - x^2})\, dx -$
     $\int_0^2 2\, dx = \frac{9}{4}\pi - 4$
4. $\int_1^3 4\, dx = 8$
5. $\left(\cos\left(-\frac{\pi}{2}\right)\right)\frac{\pi}{4} + \left(\cos\left(-\frac{\pi}{4}\right)\right)\frac{\pi}{4} +$
     $(\cos 0)\frac{\pi}{4} + \left(\cos\frac{\pi}{4}\right)\frac{\pi}{4} =$
     $\frac{\pi}{4}(\sqrt{2} + 1) \approx 1.90$
6. $\frac{1}{.5}\int_0^2 20\, dt = 80$ volts

Chapter 13 Test, Form A

(Items 1–10: 9 points each)
1. 97.5 miles
2. a. 42
    b. 46
3. $\int_2^6 \sqrt{36 - x^2}\, dx$
4. 4.5 square units
5. $-\frac{25\pi}{4}$
6. -8
7. $\int_0^2 (3x^5 + 3x^4 + 1)\, dx$
8. $2\int_0^5 (6x + 1)\, dx$, or
     $\int_0^5 (12x + 2)\, dx$

---

9. a. 36 mph
    b.

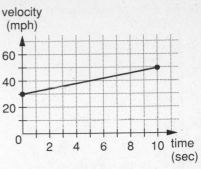

   c. about 0.111 miles, or about
        587 feet
10. a. 15π cubic units
     b. 15π cubic units
(Item 11: 10 points)
11. 133.33 m³

Chapter 13 Test, Form B
(Items 1–10: 9 points each)
1. 41.25 miles
2. a. 10
    b. 7
3. $\int_{-3}^3 (2 + \sqrt{9 - x^2})\, dx$
4. $12 + \frac{9\pi}{2} \approx 26.137$ square units
5. -38.5
6. $143\frac{1}{3}$
7. $3\int_1^{10} (x + 1)\, dx$, or
     $\int_1^{10} (3x + 3)\, dx$
8. $\int_{-1}^3 (3x^5 + x^3 - 16)\, dx$
9. a. 31 mph
    b.

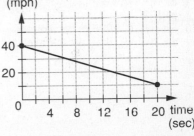

   c. about .139 miles ≈ 733 feet
10. a. $\frac{200\pi}{3}$ cubic units
     b. $\frac{200\pi}{3}$ cubic units
(Item 11: 10 points)
11. 2000π cm³, or about 6.3 liters

(Items 1–6: 7 points each)

1. 17.663

2. $\int_4^5 (x^2 + 3)\, dx$

3. $\left(\dfrac{3\sqrt{2}}{2}, -\dfrac{3\sqrt{2}}{2}\right)$ and

   $\left(-\dfrac{3\sqrt{2}}{2}, \dfrac{3\sqrt{2}}{2}\right)$

4. 528.2 ft

5. $4\sqrt{15} - 12$

6. a. $\int_0^4 (\sqrt{16 - x^2})\, dx -$

   $\int_0^4 (-x + 4)\, dx$

   b. $4\pi - 8$

(Items 7–8: 8 points each)

7. Yes, because $(-2, 1, 0) \perp M$
   and $\vec{v} = -2(-2, 1, 0)$.

8. 10.5

(Item 9: 14 points)

9. See below.

(Items 10–13: 7 points each)

10. a.

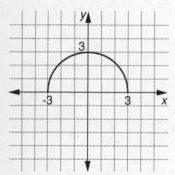

   b. 36π
   c. 36π

11. a. $-10t$ m/sec
    b. 4.47 seconds
    c. -44.7 m/sec

12. a. -7
    b. $122°$

13. Since $(-6, 12)$ can be written
    as $3(-2, 4)$, they are parallel.

(Items 1–50: 2 points each)

1. (b)
2. (d)
3. (c)
4. (c)
5. (b)
6. (d)
7. (c)
8. (a)
9. (a)
10. (c)
11. (b)
12. (d)
13. (a)
14. (b)
15. (b)
16. (d)
17. (b)
18. (c)
19. (d)
20. (a)
21. (a)
22. (c)
23. (d)
24. (b)
25. (b)
26. (c)
27. (d)
28. (b)
29. (a)
30. (b)
31. (c)
32. (d)
33. (b)
34. (b)
35. (b)
36. (c)
37. (d)
38. (a)
39. (c)
40. (c)
41. (a)
42. (a)
43. (b)
44. (a)
45. (d)
46. (d)
47. (c)
48. (d)
49. (b)
50. (a)

9.

p	q	p and q	not (p and q)	not p	not q	not p or not q
T	T	T	F	F	F	F
T	F	F	T	F	T	T
F	T	F	T	T	F	T
F	F	F	T	T	T	T

Compare these two columns.
They are the same ∴ not (p and q) ≡ (not p) or (not q).